Maths Plus

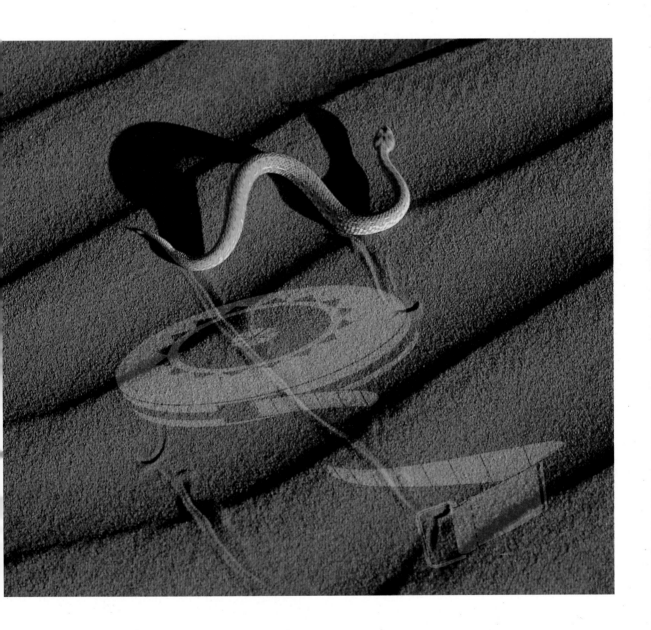

Pupil's Book 2

Published by Collins Educational
An imprint of HarperCollins*Publishers*
77–85 Fulham Palace Road,
London W6 8JB

First published 1998

ISBN 000 322486 4

The Maths Plus writing team
Sheila Beniston
Paul Cherry
Elizabeth Forth
Jill Lane
Gareth Price

Designed by Chi Leung

Picture research by Caroline Thompson

Artwork by Barking Dog Art

Printed and bound by Scotprint, Musselburgh.

Answers to questions
10.3 Estimating size

1. 3g
2. 6.5 litres
3. 250 g
4. 4 g
5. 42 kg
6. 47 litres
7. 0.5 ml
8. 2.5 litres
9. 10 g
10. 120 litres
11. 250 litres
12. 5 kg
13. 12 kg

Acknowledgements

Every effort has been made to contact the holders of copyright material, but if any have been inadvertently overlooked, the publishers will be pleased to make the necessary arrangements at the first opportunity.

The publishers would like to thank the following for permission to reproduce photographs (T = Top, B = Bottom, C = Centre, L= Left, R = Right):
Allsport/M Thompson 48, Vandystadt 62;
Austin J Brown/Aviation Picture Library 28;
C Coe/Axiom Photographic Agency 75;
BBC Photograph Library 56;
Bruce Coleman Ltd/J & D Bartlett 64T;
Lara Croft and all likenesses are the copyrighted possesion of Core Design Ltd. All Rights Reserved. 9;
Tony Waltham/Geophotos 7T, 13BR, 30L&R,;
Getty Images 4, 13CR&L, 18T, 22, 23C, 30C, 40, 41, 42, 58, 63, 66T, 76T;
Ronald Grant Archive 20T, 38, 77;
Michael Holford 12;
Adder Productions (Courtesy Kobal) 26;
Paramount (Courtesy Kobal) 55;
TriStar Pictures Inc (Courtesy Kobal) 61;
NASA 34L;
R Tyrell/Oxford Scientific Films Ltd 64R;
'PA' News Photo Library 18L;
Redferns/M Hutson 16, S King 73;
Rex Features Ltd 32, 36, 39, 46, 49, 53, 66C;
Science Photo Library 7L, 34T, 57;
The Stock Market 23T;
All other photographs supplied by Gareth Price.
Cover photograph supplied by M Fogden/Bruce Coleman Ltd.

Contents

7 ◆ Shape

7.1 Sailing

Sailing ships may not be as fast as liners with diesel engines – but they look better! And can you imagine a surfboard with an engine?

- *What advantages do sails have for ships?*
- *How many different shapes can you see in the sails?*

Three sides

Some of the sails are **triangles**. All triangles have three straight sides. There are different kinds of triangles. **Equilateral** triangles have sides of all the same length. **Isosceles** triangles have two sides of the same length. **Scalene** triangles have three different sides.

Sort these three-sided shapes into the correct groups. ①

Isosceles triangles	Equilateral triangles	Right-angled triangles	Scalene triangles

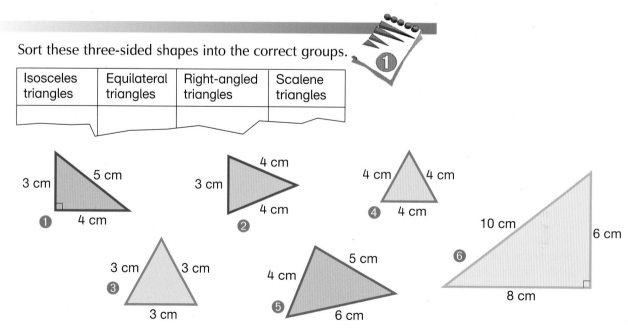

4

Four sides

Some of the sails have four sides. All shapes with four sides are called **quadrilaterals**. There are different names for different types of quadrilateral. A **square** has sides which are all the same length and all the angles are equal.

Name		Are any sides parallel?	Are any sides the same length?	Are there any right angles?
Square		opposite sides parallel	all the same length	all corners are right angles
Parallelogram		opposite sides parallel	opposite sides are the same length	no right angles
Trapezium		one pair of opposite sides are parallel	no sides have the same length	up to two right angles possible
Kite		no sides parallel	the two sides next to each other are the same length	up to one right angle possible
Rhombus		opposite sides parallel	all sides are the same length	no right angles
Rectangle		opposite sides are parallel	opposite sides are the same length	all angles are right angles

Sort these four-sided shapes into the correct group.

Rectangle	Parallelogram	Trapezium	Square	Kite	Rhombus

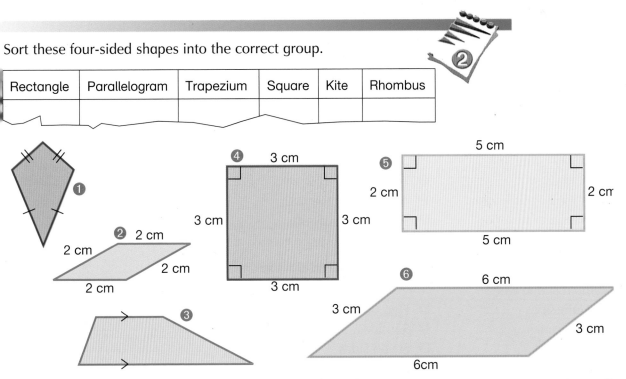

5

Counting corners

Sails must be fixed at the **corners**. Sometimes they are also fixed along an **edge**. A triangular sail must have at least three fixing points. If any of these points are broken the sail will not work properly. Which do you think is safer – a sail fixed along one edge or a sail fixed at a corner? Why?

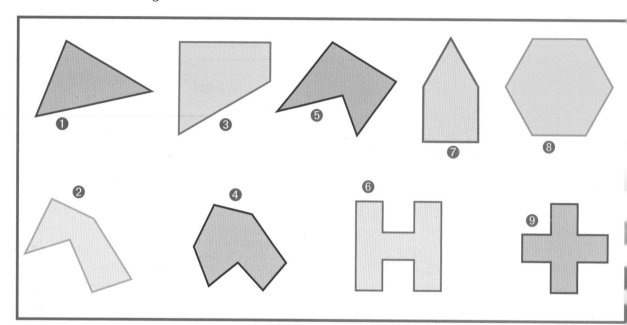

Write down the number of corners on each of the shapes in the blue box.

Write down the number of edges on each of the shapes in the blue box.

Use an angle measurer to construct the following shapes accurately.

1. A square
2. A regular pentagon
3. A regular hexagon
4. A triangle
5. A regular octagon
6. A regular decagon

Name a shape with:

1. Eight sides
2. Nine sides
3. Ten sides
4. Five sides
5. Six sides
6. Seven sides

7.2 Straight edges

The photographs show **three-dimensional** shapes made of flat plates with straight edges joined together. Each plate is called a **face**. The more plates there are the smoother the shape can be.

- *List as many three-dimensional shapes as you can that are made of flat plates with straight edges.*
- *How many edges do you think there are in the picture of the golfball radar dome?*

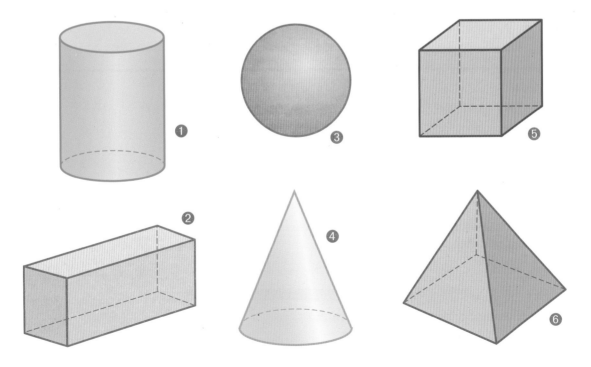

Name each of these 3D shapes.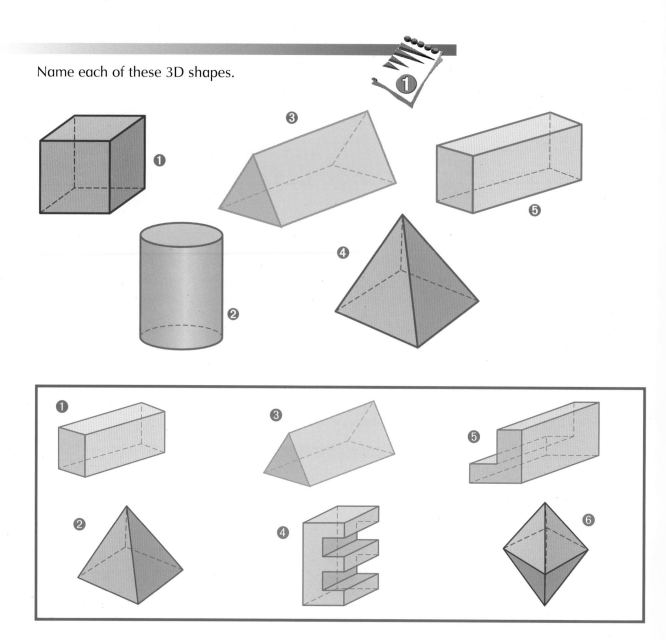

Write down the number of corners on each of the shapes in the blue box.

Write down the number of edges on each of the shapes in the blue box.

Write down the number of faces on each of the shapes in the blue box.

7.3 Computer drawings

Lara Croft is the first virtual sex symbol! She is a character in a computer game and is made up of thousands of flat faces joined together on the screen.

- *Have you played on a computer game system?*
  Which one?
- *What sorts of games do you like best?*

Making the rules

The rules the computer uses to draw Lara are the same as the rules you can use to draw simple shapes on a small computer. The computer language guides a pen across the screen. As the pen moves it leaves a line. You can draw simple shapes by telling the pen how to move. The computer draws a line in the direction the arrow is pointing.

The simplest language for drawing on a computer screen is LOGO.

Instruction	What you see on the screen
Forward 40	——————————▶
Forward 80	————————————————————▶

Programs

Each instructions is called a **command**. A collection of commands is called a **program**. The computer follows instructions in order. So, if you put commands together, you can make lines with bends.

Instructions	What you see on the screen
Forward 40	
Right turn 90	
Forward 40	

Put enough commands together and you can draw a square on the screen.

Commands	What you see on the screen
Forward 40	
Right turn 90	
Forward 40	
Right turn 90	
Forward 40	
Right turn 90	
Forward 40	
Right turn 90	

Simple commands

LOGO is a powerful language that uses simple commands. These commands will cover almost everything you need to do.

Command	Shortcut	What the computer does
Forward 40	FD 40	Moves forward 40 units
Backward 40	BK 40	Moves backwards 40 units
Turn right	RT 90	Turns right by 90°
Turn left	LT 90	Turns left by 90°
Clear screen	CS	Clears all the lines off the screen
Hide turtle	HT	Hides the turtle – you can't see where the pen is
Show turtle	ST	Makes the turtle show up on the screen

Be very careful with commands and spaces. FD 40 works, but sometimes commands don't do what you expect!

Explain what is wrong in each of these commands.
❶ FDD 40   ❸ FFDD 4
❷ FD40   ❹ FD04

Write the LOGO commands for the following tasks.
❶ Go forwards 20 units.
❷ Go backwards 50 units.
❸ Clear the screen.
❹ Put the turtle in the centre of the screen.
❺ Stop the turtle drawing.
❻ Turn right 60°.
❼ Turn left 45°.
❽ Draw a square, sides length 40 units.
❾ Draw an equilateral triangle, sides 70 units.
❿ A short program to draw a regular decagon with sides of 10 units.

Write out a set of LOGO instructions to draw the following shapes. Print out copies of each shape.
❶ Square   ❹ Regular octagon
❷ Regular hexagon   ❺ Regular decagon
❸ Equilateral triangle ❻ Square with sides 50 units long

7.4 Fitting together

This wall is decorated with lots of small tiles. The pieces fit together and cover the whole area without any gaps. This is called a **mosaic**.

- *Why do people make mosaics?*
- *What different shaped tiles can you see in the first picture?*

The mosaic in the photograph uses small square tiles. Squares fit together without any gaps. This is called a **tessellation**. Not every shape can **tessellate** to make a pattern with no gaps.

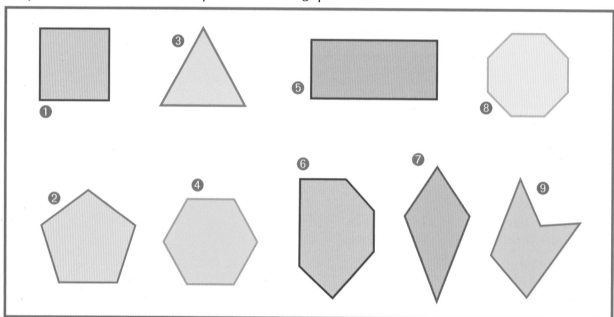

Which of the shapes in the blue box can tessellate?

Draw three different tessellating patterns using shapes from the blue box.

Copy these tessellations on to squared paper.
Complete them to fill all the space available.

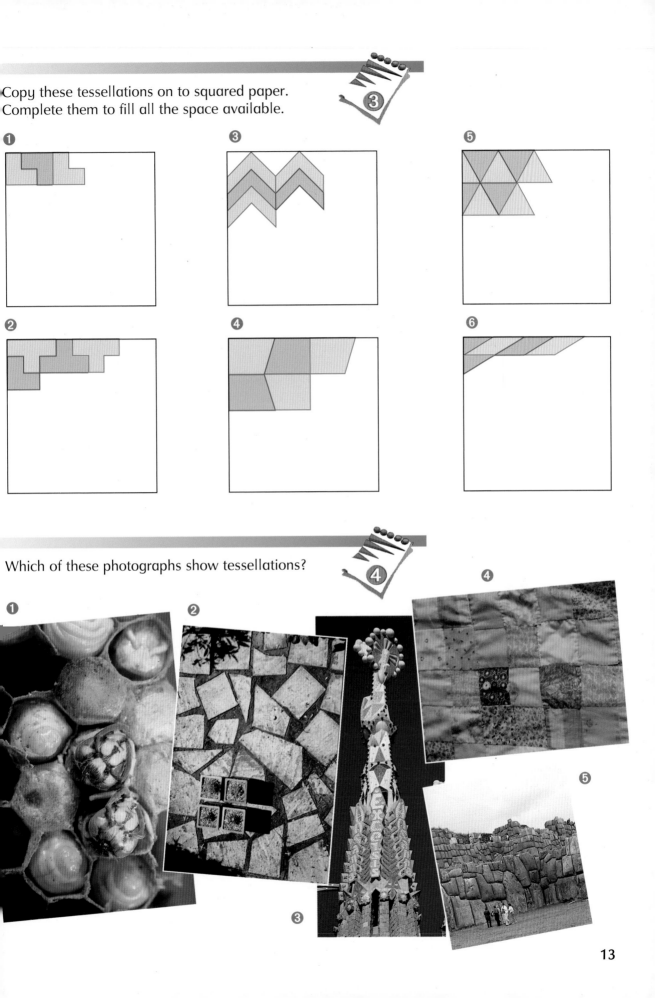

3

1

3

5

2

4

6

Which of these photographs show tessellations?

4

1

2

3

4

5

7.5 It's a wrap!

All the boxes in the photograph were made from a single sheet of card. The manufacturer folded the card to make an interesting three-dimensional shape. Designers produce patterns for the shapes called **nets**. A net shows the fold lines to make a three-dimensional shape.

- *Why do people package chocolates in different shaped containers?*
- *How do they make the containers?*

You can make some containers by cutting and folding a single flat piece of paper or card. We can draw a net for any three-dimensional object so long as it has flat faces and straight edges. We can even draw nets for some shapes with curved sides.

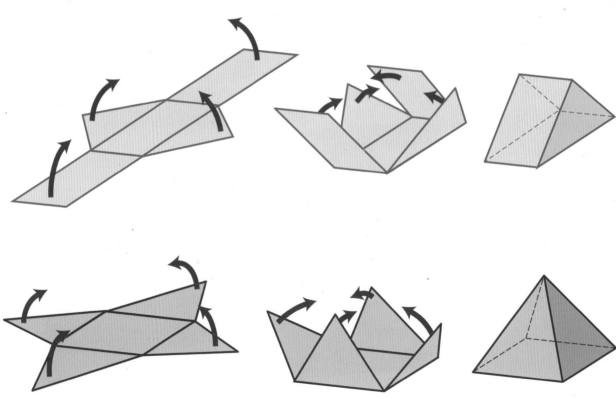

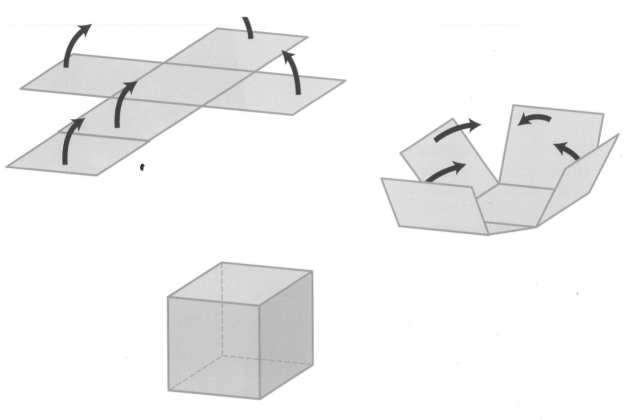

Use polydrons to make a 3D shape. Unfold it to make a net. Now draw round it to make a template on card.
Make at least four 3D shapes in this way.

Draw a net for each of these solids.

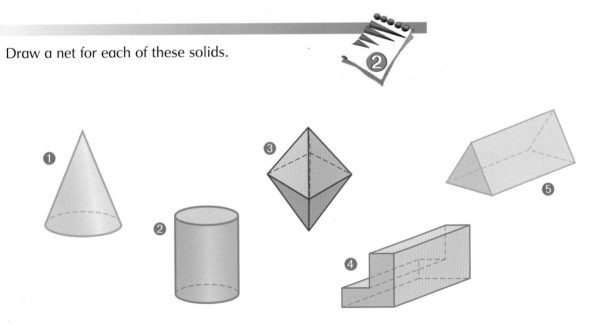

7.6 Which is your best side?

Your face is a very complicated shape. It's not surprising the two halves don't quite match. A simpler shape like a square can be divided into two halves. The line that divides the shape is called a line of **symmetry**.

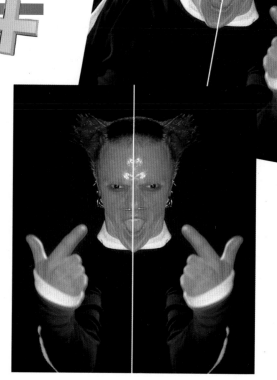

- *Which picture of Keith Flint do you think is best? Why?*
- *Which is your 'best side'?*

These are the four lines of symmetry for a square.

Copy these shapes into your book. Now draw all the lines of symmetry on each of these shapes.

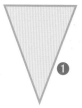

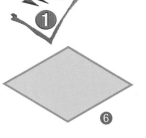
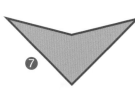

If you have half of a symmetrical shape you can draw the other half using a mirror line.
Copy these symmetrical pictures into your book and complete them.

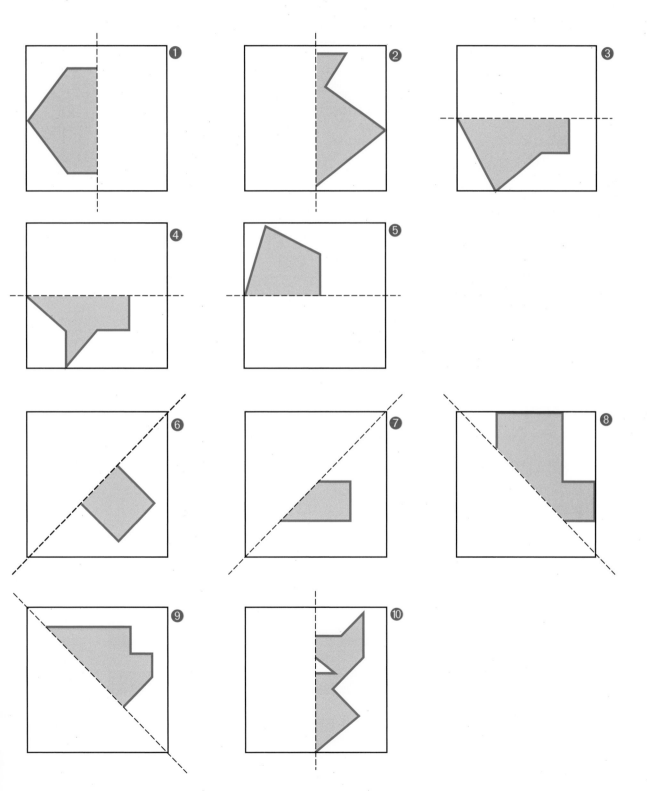

Fly the flag

Some flags are symmetrical. This is good because it doesn't matter which way up you fly the flag. Look at the two flags in the photograph below. At least one is symmetrical – which one? And is the other symmetrical?

Copy these flags into your book. Now draw in the lines of symmetry.

①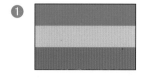

②

③

④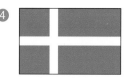

⑤

⑥

⑦

⑧

⑨

18

Copy these flags into your book. Now complete the other half of these symmetrical flags.

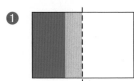

①

④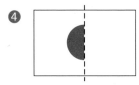

⑦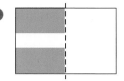

②

⑤

⑧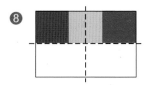

③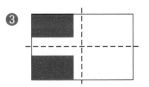

⑥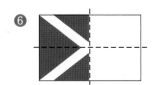

⑨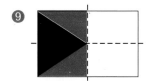

Between the covers

A book jacket is sometimes symmetrical. The line of symmetry is the spine. Often the main difference between the front and back cover is the title. If you take away the words you do end up with an almost symmetrical background design.

Draw a book cover with a symmetrical background design. You can make up a book that does not exist or draw one with a story you know. Remember the cover must be symmetrical and give people an idea of what is in the book.

7.7 Scale drawings

A **scale model** is not just a smaller version of the real thing. All the measurements must be in the correct proportions. So, if the laser cannon is four times smaller than real life, the radar mast must be four times smaller as well. If different parts are reduced by different amounts the whole model goes wrong.

- *Did you collect scale models? How accurate were the models?*
- *Why do film makers use scale models rather than the real thing?*

Model makers often use fractions to show how many times smaller the model is compared with the real thing. A 1:24 model is 24 times smaller than the real thing.

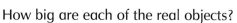

How tall are each of these models?
1. A 1:12 model of a 24 m high tower
2. A 1:6 model of a 6 foot tall film star
3. A 1:100 model of a 200 m long airship
4. A 1:250 model of the 125 m high Saturn V rocket
5. A 1:5 model of 25 m long railway carriage

How big are each of the real objects?
1. A 1:20 model of a speeder bike is 21 cm long.
2. A 1:10 model of an elephant is 31 cm tall.
3. A 1:52 model of a submarine is 112 cm long.
4. A 1:150 model of an Egyptian pyramid is 1 m high.
5. A 1:64 model of a dinosaur stands 20 cm tall.

Scale drawings

Scale drawings use the same rules as scale models. A line on the page represents a length in the rule world. So, in a 1:100 scale drawing a 1 cm line would represent a 100 cm length.

How big are each of the rooms shown in these scale drawings?

0   1 metre

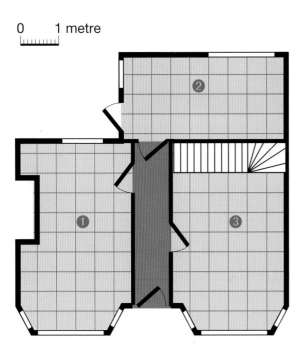

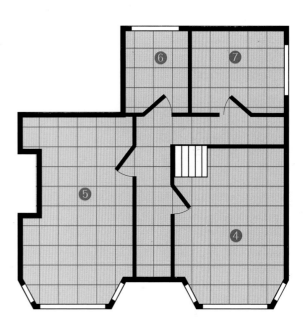

Draw a scale drawing of a room at home. Mark on important measurements like doors and windows.

Look at the scale drawing of the entrance hall shown in red in exercise 3. My piano measures 70 cm wide by 155 cm long and 130 cm high. Could I get my piano through the entrance hall and into the front room?

◆8 Space

8.1 Take your seats

This stadium has thousands of seats. If you've paid for a good seat you want to know exactly where it is!

* *What was the last time you went to a large stadium or hall?*
* *Were you given a particular seat or could you go anywhere in a certain area?*

The Big Match
* Upper tier
* Row 27   **£6.50**
* Seat 41

Your ticket shows you which seat is yours. To find this seat you must first go to the upper tier. Then find row 27. Go along row 27 until you get to the seat labelled 41. That is your place!

This system works a bit like the stadium seating plan. The red cross is at position (**3, 2**). The blue cross has the co-ordinates (**3, 5**).

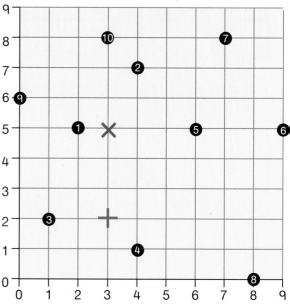

Give the co-ordinates of each of the points ❶ to ❿ on the diagram.

Draw a grid like the one above into your book. On your grid plot each of these points and label them ❶ to ⑫.

❶ (5,2)	❹ (0,4)	❼ (3,9)	❿ (5,5)
❷ (6,4)	❺ (7,3)	❽ (6,7)	⑪ (4,7)
❸ (1,5)	❻ (9,3)	❾ (6,0)	⑫ (9,1)

Map references

Travel guides to cities often use grid references to find places on maps. New York City is built on a grid pattern so it's always easy to know where you are.

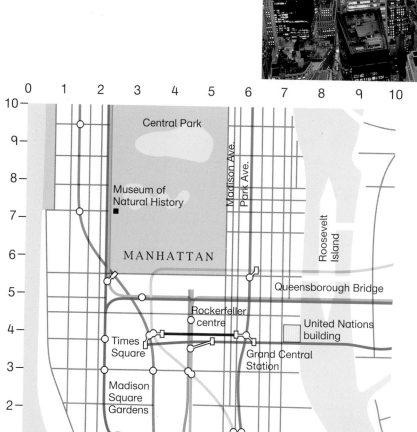

The references identify a complete square on the grid. So, (B,2) identifies the square outlined in red in the map above. Geographers often use grid references without the brackets or the comma between. (B,2) can be written as B2. The large map on the next page uses four figure references. Heathrow airport is at position 0151. The 01 is the horizontal reference and the 51 is the vertical refernce.

What would you find at each of these grid references on the map of New York?

① C2
② C4
③ E4
④ G3
⑤ C7
⑥ H3

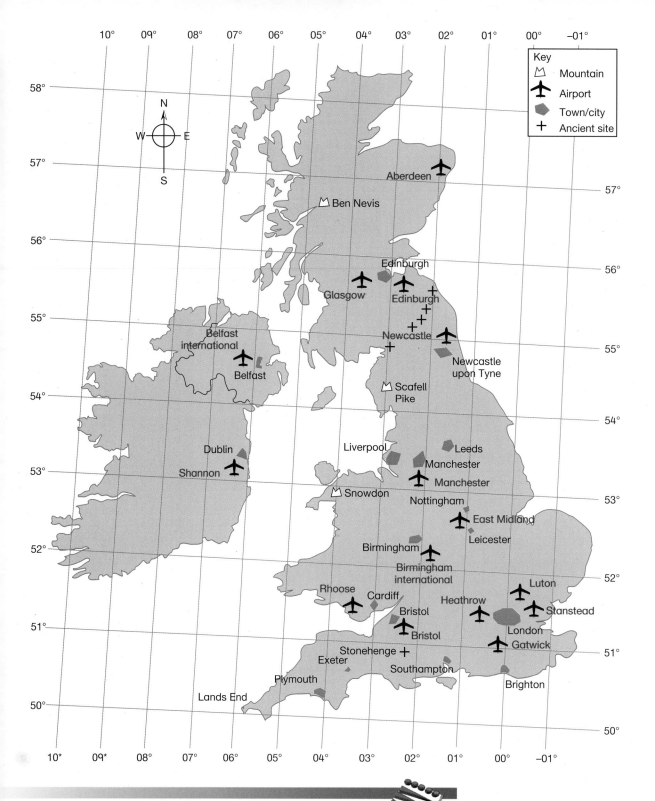

What feature can you find at each of these grid references on the map of the UK?

❶ 0352

❷ 0650

❸ 0556

❹ 0250

❺ 0257

What is the grid reference for each of these airports?

1. Bristol
2. Luton
3. Belfast International
4. Edinburgh
5. Stansted
6. Rhoose
7. Glasgow
8. Shannon

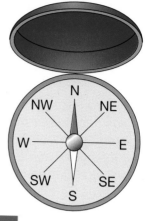

Clear directions

A compass uses a different system to help you find your way around. The direction you need to go in is given a name. There are four major directions. The ones in between are mixtures of these four. To use a compass you must make sure the north line points directly to the North Pole.

Which direction is shown by each of these compasses?

1. Is Heathrow north, south-East or west of London?
2. Which London airport is north-east of the city?
3. Which airport is due west of Edinburgh airport?
4. What direction is Birmingham International airport from East Midlands airport?
5. What direction is Newcastle airport from Birmingham International airport?
6. If I fly due east from Shannon airport which is the first airport I will see?
7. Which direction will I have to fly to get from Luton airport to Bristol airport?

8.2 Secret messages

Spies use codes to send messages. A code must be easy for your friend to understand but impossible for your enemies to use. Many businesses also use codes, for example to transfer money and documents around the world across the INTERNET.

- *When might you need a secure code? (Think about your bank account, credit card number, even your telephone number.)*
- *Do you feel sure that no-one can break into your bank account?*

Carrying messages

One simple type of code uses a grid. Each letter fits on one point in this simple 5 x 5 grid. This time the letters are placed at the point where the lines intersect. A grid reference marks a complete square but the **co-ordinates** mark a tiny point. This makes the co-ordinates much more accurate than a grid reference.

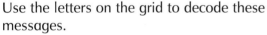

Use the letters on the grid to decode these messages.

❶ (2,4) (1,3) (1,3) (2,5)   (4,3) (5,1) (3,5) (5,3)!

❷ (3,1) (3,4) (1,3)   (3,1) (5,5) (2,3) (5,2) (4,2)
(5,2) (1,3)   (4,5) (1,5)   (5,5)
(3,3) (4,4) (4,3) (4,3) (4,4) (1,3) (2,3) (5,5) (4,4)
(3,2) (1,5)?
I do!

❸ (2,3) (1,3) (3,1)   (3,1) (1,5)   (5,3) (2,3) (1,3) (3,1)
(3,1) (3,4) (5,5) (5,2)   (5,2) (1,3)   (2,5) (1,3)

❹ (3,3) (5,5) (5,2) (3,4) (4,2)   (1,2) (4,3) (5,1) (4,2)
(3,2) (1,3) (3,5) (5,3) (4,2) !

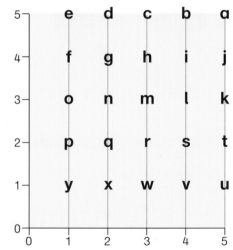

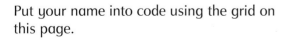

Put your name into code using the grid on this page.

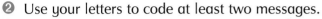

1. Draw a grid like the one for exercise 1 but put the letters in different positions.
2. Use your letters to code at least two messages.
3. Ask a friend to decode your messages.
   Remember to give him or her a copy of your grid.

Making pictures

Co-ordinates can be very accurate. They identify a single point in a grid. If you join these points with lines you can produce some very accurate drawings. This shape uses just five lines to make a three dimensional picture of a cross.

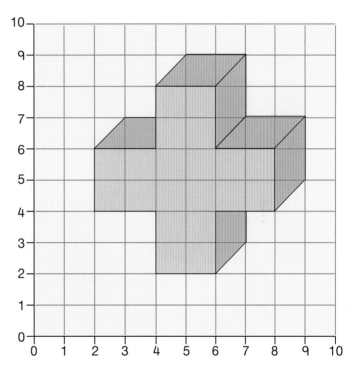

Draw a 10 x 10 grid in your book. Plot these points in turn on your grid. Join each point carefully to the one before it.

(1,1) (1,6) (4,9) (7,6) (1,6) (7,1) (1,1) (7,6) (7,1)

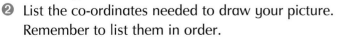

1. Draw a very simple straight line picture on a 10 x 10 grid.
2. List the co-ordinates needed to draw your picture.
   Remember to list them in order.
3. Give your co-ordinates list to a friend and ask him or her to draw a copy of your picture.

27

8.3 Round we go

When you loop the loop your plane turns right over as it flies
along. In the middle of the turn you are completely upside down!
When the loop is finished the plane is the right way up again.
We say it has **rotated** through a complete turn.

Shapes can be rotated too. You must decide which point the shape
rotates around and then turn it as far as you need.

- *Have you ever seen an old plane like this? When
  was that?*
- *What do you think it would be like to fly upside
  down?*

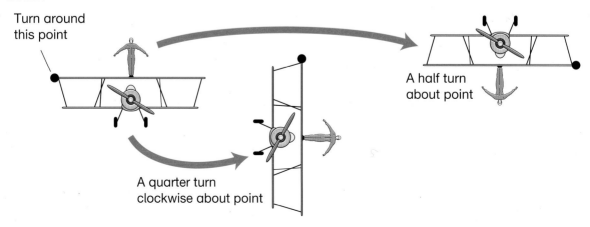

Turn around
this point

A half turn
about point

A quarter turn
clockwise about point

Rotate each of these shapes through a half turn about the dot. Draw what the shape looks like now.

Rotate each of these shapes clockwise through a quarter turn about the dot. Draw what the shape looks like now.

8.4 The right angle!

The corners in most buildings are 90°. This is called a **right angle**. Many builders can tell if an angle is a right angle by looking at it. This is useful because it helps them to build straight walls or plaster over the corners neatly in a house. How good are you at recognising right angles?

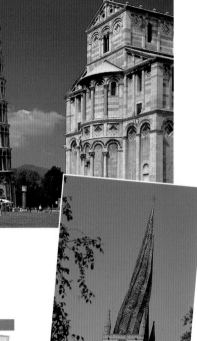

- *List any buildings you know that do not stand up straight.*
- *Why do they lean over?*

Look at all the right angles around the room.
List at least five right angles that you can see.

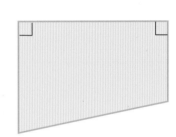

We mark the right angles in a shape with a small square. A rectangle has four right angles.

Redraw the shapes below and mark all the right angles with a square.

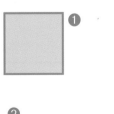
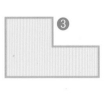
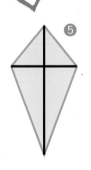

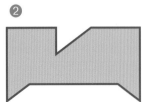
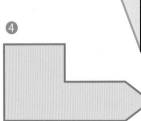
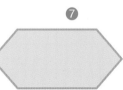

Right or not?

Mathematicians sort angles into three main groups.

Look carefully at each of these angles. Do not measure them.

Is the angle larger than, smaller than or equal to a right angle?

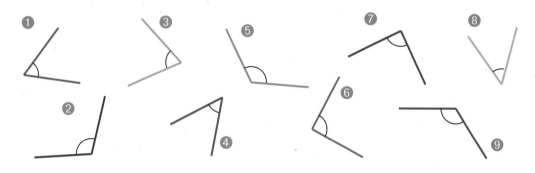

Look carefully at each of these angles. Do not measure them.

Is the angle acute, obtuse or reflex?

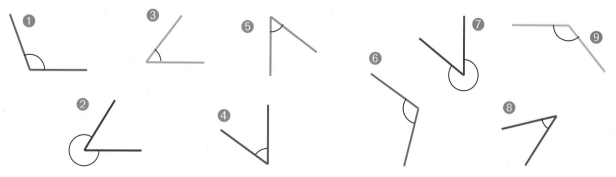

8.5 Estimating and measuring angles

He looks more comfortable than I would be like that! Contortionists seem to be able to bend into impossible shapes. But what damage are they doing to their bodies?

- *Would you like to be this supple? Why?*
- *Do you think stretching like this is bad for your body? Why?*

Estimate the size of the angles ❶ to ❽. Do not measure them.

Estimate the size of these angles. Do not measure them.

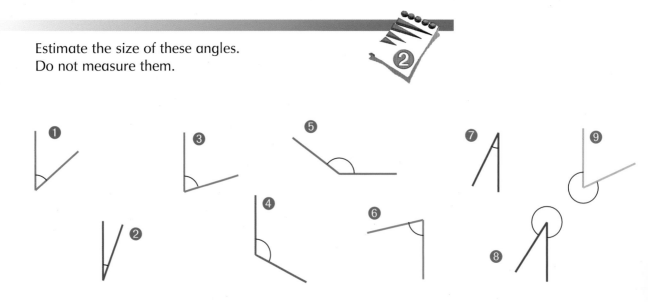

32

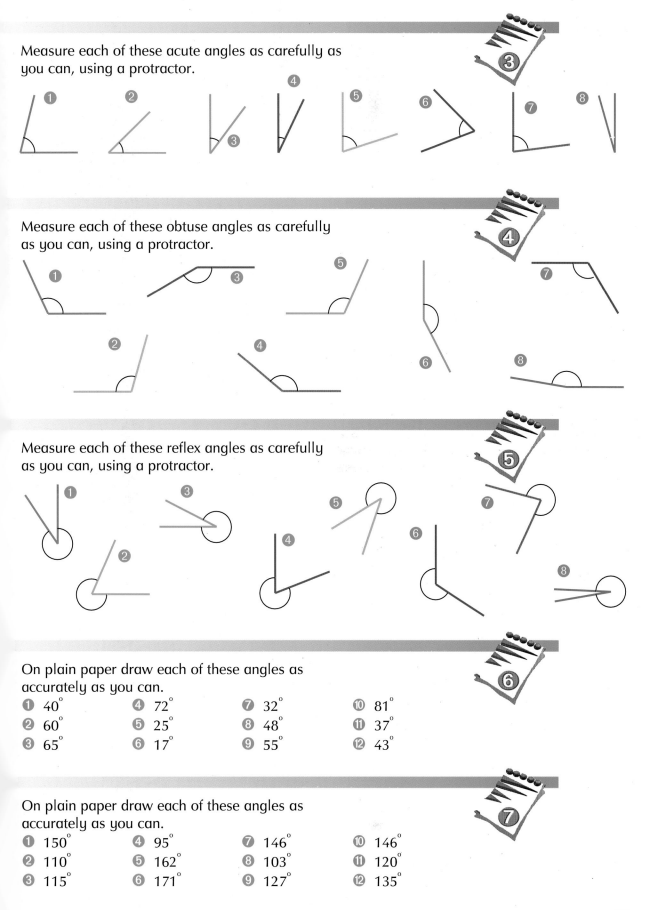

Measure each of these acute angles as carefully as you can, using a protractor.

Measure each of these obtuse angles as carefully as you can, using a protractor.

Measure each of these reflex angles as carefully as you can, using a protractor.

On plain paper draw each of these angles as accurately as you can.

1 $40°$ 4 $72°$ 7 $32°$ 10 $81°$
2 $60°$ 5 $25°$ 8 $48°$ 11 $37°$
3 $65°$ 6 $17°$ 9 $55°$ 12 $43°$

On plain paper draw each of these angles as accurately as you can.

1 $150°$ 4 $95°$ 7 $146°$ 10 $146°$
2 $110°$ 5 $162°$ 8 $103°$ 11 $120°$
3 $115°$ 6 $171°$ 9 $127°$ 12 $135°$

Calendars, time and money

9.1 Long time no see

The Mir space station was launched on February 20th 1986. It lasted over ten years in orbit until finally crashing in 1997. The photograph shows astronaut Shannon Lucid leaving Mir in September 1996 after six months in space – the longest time any American had ever spent in space.

- *What would you miss most if you went to a space station?*
- *How would you feel when you finally got home?*

Convert the following days into weeks and days.

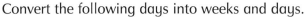

❶ 12 days   ❹ 51 days   ❼ 29 days   ❿ 10 days
❷ 32 days   ❺ 40 days   ❽ 39 days   ⓫ 17 days
❸ 27 days   ❻ 35 days   ❾ 42 days   ⓬ 112 days

Convert the following weeks and days into days.

❶ 2 weeks 5 days   ❺ 10 weeks 3 days   ❾ 17 weeks 2 days
❷ 4 weeks 1 day   ❻ 4 weeks 6 days   ❿ 2 weeks 3 days
❸ 7 weeks 6 days   ❼ 6 weeks 2 days   ⓫ 2 weeks 1 day
❹ 9 weeks 2 days   ❽ 11 weeks 3 days   ⓬ 5 weeks 2 days

Pay day!

Many jobs are paid by the hour. So, if you do an eight-hour shift you get eight times the pay for a single hour. A normal working week is 40 hours. How much will you get paid for a full week if you get £4 an hour?

How much is each of these people paid per week?

1. Rashid works five days each week as a trainee chef. He earns £35 per day.
2. Gabrielle is paid £123 per day as a solicitor. She works for three days each week.
3. Percy is the penguin keeper at the local zoo. He works six days every week and earns £21.50 per day.
4. Leon is a hairdresser in a large salon. He earns £23 per day and does a six-day week.
5. Shushmita works at the local firestation. She earns £66.50 a day for a four-day week.

Overtime

Sometimes you are paid extra for weekend work or overtime. If overtime is paid at time and a half, it means you are paid one and a half hours for every hour you work. If you are paid £4 per hour and you work an extra 4 hours over the weekend, how much overtime pay will you get?

1. Chris earns £48 per hour as a financial adviser. If he works a forty hour week and 4 hours overtime how much is he paid?
2. Polly works at Happy Pets and earns £4.50 an hour for a 35 hour week. She does an extra six hours one week. How much is she paid that week?
3. William earns £32 per hour. He does 12 hours overtime one weekend. How much does his overtime pay come to?
4. Elizabeth is paid £12 per hour for a 40 hour week. One week she works 48 hours in total. How much does she earn that week?
5. Jaz does 4 hours on a Saturday for £16 in total. His boss asks him to work two hours extra and he will pay him overtime for those two hours. What is his total pay that week?

First convert the time to hours: 40

↓

Then multiply the hours by your pay per hour:
40 x £4 = £160

↓

Your weekly pay is: £160.

First convert the the time to hours: 4 x 1 ½ = 6 hours

↓

Then multiply the hours by your pay per hour:
6 x £4 = £24

↓

You are paid £24 for your overtime. Now add this to your basic wage:
£160 + £24 = £184

↓

So, your wage for the week is £184.

9.2 Grandma at 15!

Just like other teenagers Doris loves to spend time hanging out at the beach surfing and working on her tan. However, Doris has less time than most 15 year-olds because a few days ago she became a grandmother. Doris was born on February 29th 1936, which means that she has only had 15 birthdays so far. This is because February only has 29 days once in every four years. We call this a **leap year**. In an ordinary year, there are only 28 days in February.

- *When is your birthday?*
- *If you had been born on February 29th, would you still celebrate a birthday each year? When would you celebrate it?*

The number of days in each month below is correct – but the months are in the wrong order. Sort them into the correct order. ①

April 30	February 28	August 31
	March 31	June 30
July 31	January 31	September 30
December 31	October 31	May 31	November 30

List all the months of the year with 31 days. ②

List all the months of the year with only 30 days. ③

Match these events to the correct time of the year.
Put each one in the correct month.

❶ Christmas

❹ New Year's Eve

❼ Hogmanay

❽ Valentine's day

❷ Wimbledon

❺ Hallowe'en

❾ Mothering Sunday

❸ Bonfire Night

❻ Start of the football season

❿ Longest day of the year

Explain what is meant by a leap year.

How many days in each of the following?

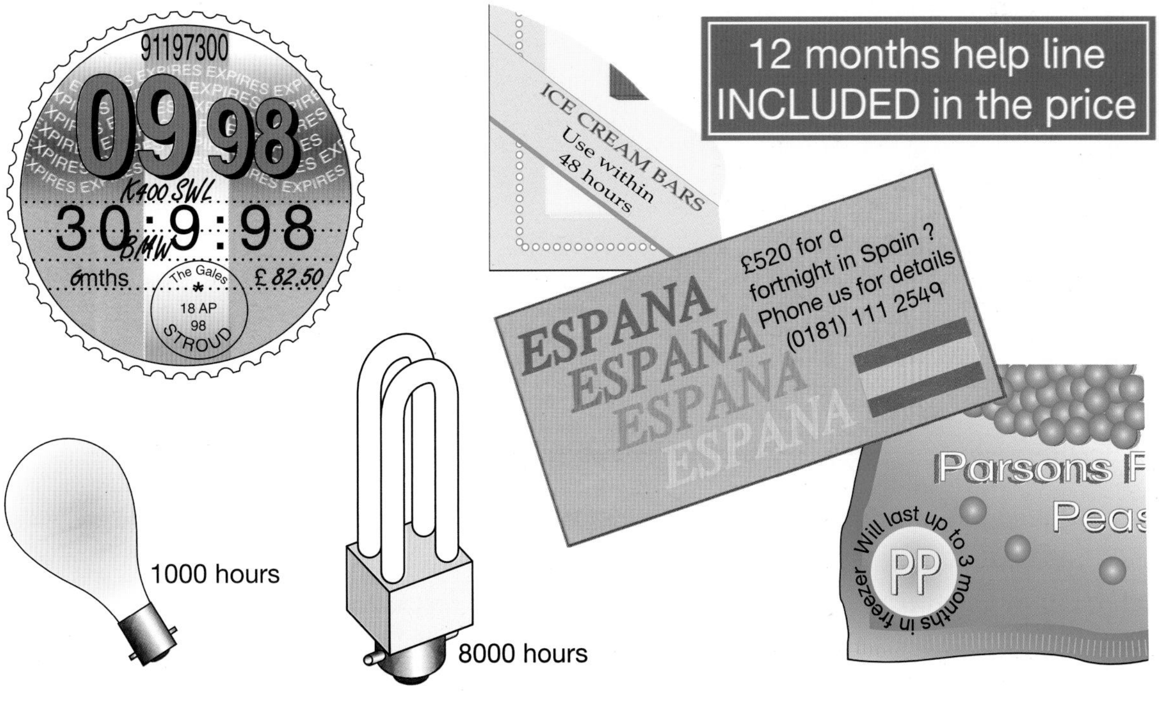

91197300

09 98

K400.SWL

30 : 9 : 98

BMW

6mths

£ 82.50

The Gales

18 AP 98

STROUD

ICE CREAM BARS
Use within 48 hours

12 months help line INCLUDED in the price

ESPANA
ESPANA
ESPANA
ESPANA
ESPANA

£520 for a fortnight in Spain? Phone us for details (0181) 111 2549

1000 hours

8000 hours

Parsons F Peas

Will last up to 3 months in freezer

PP

9.3 Unlucky for some

Ever had one of those days when everything seems to go wrong? Some people are so keen to avoid bad luck they won't leave their home on Friday 13th. For this driver, that would have been a good idea!

- *Why do some people think that Friday 13th is unlucky?*
- *Do you have any lucky or unlucky dates? When are they?*

JANUARY						
M	T	W	T	F	S	S
				1	2	3
4	5	6	7	8	9	10
11	12	13	14	15	16	17
18	19	20	21	22	23	24
25	26	27	28	29	30	31

FEBRUARY						
M	T	W	T	F	S	S
1	2	3	4	5	6	7
8	9	10	11	12	13	14
15	16	17	18	19	20	21
22	23	24	25	26	27	28

MARCH						
M	T	W	T	F	S	S
1	2	3	4	5	6	7
8	9	10	11	12	13	14
15	16	17	18	19	20	21
22	23	24	25	26	27	28
29	30	31				

APRIL						
M	T	W	T	F	S	S
			1	2	3	4
5	6	7	8	9	10	11
12	13	14	15	16	17	18
19	20	21	22	23	24	25
26	27	28	29	30		

MAY						
M	T	W	T	F	S	S
					1	2
3	4	5	6	7	8	9
10	11	12	13	14	15	16
17	18	19	20	21	22	23
24	25	26	27	28	29	30
31						

JUNE						
M	T	W	T	F	S	S
	1	2	3	4	5	6
7	8	9	10	11	12	13
14	15	16	17	18	19	20
21	22	23	24	25	26	27
28	29	30				

JULY						
M	T	W	T	F	S	S
			1	2	3	4
5	6	7	8	9	10	11
12	13	14	15	16	17	18
19	20	21	22	23	24	25
26	27	28	29	30	31	

AUGUST						
M	T	W	T	F	S	S
						1
2	3	4	5	6	7	8
9	10	11	12	13	14	15
16	17	18	19	20	21	22
23	24	25	26	27	28	29
30	31					

SEPTEMBER						
M	T	W	T	F	S	S
	1	2	3	4	5	
6	7	8	9	10	11	12
13	14	15	16	17	18	19
20	21	22	23	24	25	26
27	28	29	30			

OCTOBER						
M	T	W	T	F	S	S
				1	2	3
4	5	6	7	8	9	10
11	12	13	14	15	16	17
18	19	20	21	22	23	24
25	26	27	28	29	30	31

NOVEMBER						
M	T	W	T	F	S	S
1	2	3	4	5	6	7
8	9	10	11	12	13	14
15	16	17	18	19	20	21
22	23	24	25	26	27	28
29	30					

DECEMBER						
M	T	W	T	F	S	S
		1	2	3	4	5
6	7	8	9	10	11	12
13	14	15	16	17	18	19
20	21	22	23	24	25	26
27	28	29	30	31		

Use the calendar above to answer the following questions.

❶ What day is January 1st?
❷ What day is Christmas Day?
❸ What is the last day in October?
❹ What date is the first Wednesday in May?
❺ What date is the last Thursday in August?
❻ What date is the first Monday in September?

How many days are there between the following dates?

❶ 3rd February to 18th February
❷ 6th June to 13th June
❸ 11th September to 30th September
❹ 13th December to 31st December
❺ 2nd April to 21st April
❻ 9th October to 22nd October

How many weeks and days are there between the following dates?

❶ 4th January to 9th March
❷ 6th April to 11th July
❸ 12th July to 3rd August
❹ 5th September to 20th December
❺ 20th October to 22nd December
❻ 13th April to 30th June

Making babies

Madonna gave birth to her first child, Lourdes Maria Ciccone Leon on October 14, 1996. She could estimate when the baby would be born. Of course, most babies don't arrive exactly on time, but it is useful to have a date to plan for. The baby should be born 281 days after the start of the mother's last period. Most babies arrive within two weeks either side of the calculated date.

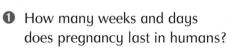

❶ How many weeks and days does pregnancy last in humans?
❷ If someone becomes pregant on January 1st when will the baby probably be born?

❶ How many weeks and days does preganancy last in lions?
❷ If a pig becomes pregnant on March 1st when will the piglets be born?
❸ A tiger pregnancy lasts 15 weeks and 2 days. Is this longer or shorter than a pig's?
❹ How long does pregnancy last in an elephant in months?
❺ A hedgehog is pregnant for five weeks. How many days is that?

Animal	Length of pregnancy / days
Rabbit	31
Ferret	42
Lion	107
Pig	113
Human	266
Camel	315
Zebra	400
Elephant	700

39

9.4 Time off

FULLY INCLUSIVE:
* Instructions * Full board accommodation *
* All equipment included * Full-on cave safaris *
* Local transport * All prices include VAT *

FIVE-DAY CAVING WEEKS   £288

The five-day week includes five full days caving with five nights full
board accommodation and starts at 6.00 pm on Sunday evening
through until Friday at 4.30 pm. Accommodation for Friday night
can be arranged.

CAVING WEEKEND   £123

The weekends include two full days caving and accommodation for
Friday and Saturday night with meals from Saturday breakfast to
Sunday lunch inclusive. Weekends begin 7.00–11.00 pm Friday and
finish at 4.30 pm Sunday.

CAVING BANK HOLIDAY THREE DAY BREAKS   £177

May Day Bank Holiday 1st – 4th May. Spring Bank Holiday
22nd – 25th May. August Bank Holiday 28th – 31st.
The Bank Holiday three-day breaks include three full days caving
with accommodation for Friday to Sunday night inclusive. (Meals
from Saturday breakfast to Monday lunch inclusive.) The breaks
begin 7.00 pm – 11.00 pm Friday and finish at 4.30 pm on Monday.
Please note that two-day weekends can also be taken over all Bank
Holiday Weekends.

FIRST AID COURSES   £35

One-day courses run on the first monday of every month. Check for
availability of places – booking in advance is essential.

Activity holidays are very popular now. Of course, you may end up
with a broken leg if you try too many activities and you're not very
good at them!

- *Which activities would you want to do?*
- *What else would you like to be able to do on holiday?*

❶ How much does it cost to go on a Caving Bank
  Holiday three-day break?
❷ What time on Sunday does the Caving Weekend finish?
❸ On a five-day Caving Week what is the earliest time
  I can start?
❹ When can I go on the one-day First Aid Course?
❺ How much will it cost to go on a five-day Caving Week?

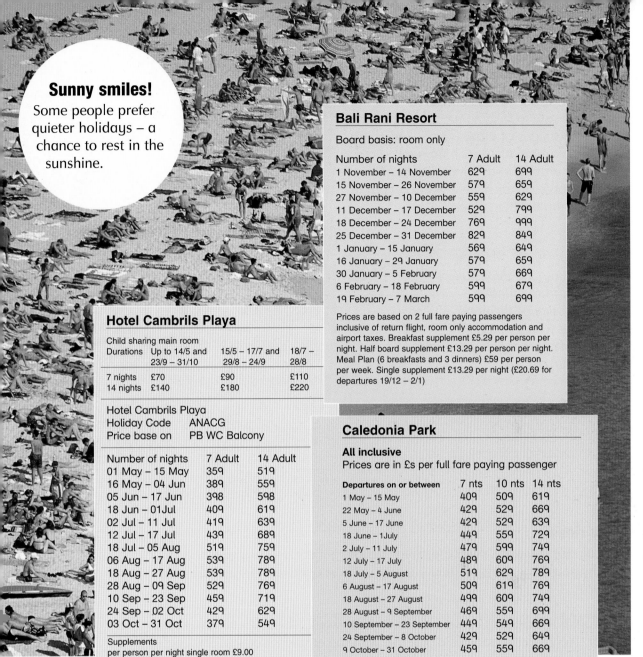

Sunny smiles!

Some people prefer quieter holidays – a chance to rest in the sunshine.

Bali Rani Resort

Board basis: room only

Number of nights	7 Adult	14 Adult
1 November – 14 November	629	699
15 November – 26 November	579	659
27 November – 10 December	559	629
11 December – 17 December	529	799
18 December – 24 December	769	999
25 December – 31 December	829	849
1 January – 15 January	569	649
16 January – 29 January	579	659
30 January – 5 February	579	669
6 February – 18 February	599	679
19 February – 7 March	599	699

Prices are based on 2 full fare paying passengers inclusive of return flight, room only accommodation and airport taxes. Breakfast supplement £5.29 per person per night. Half board supplement £13.29 per person per night. Meal Plan (6 breakfasts and 3 dinners) £59 per person per week. Single supplement £13.29 per night (£20.69 for departures 19/12 – 2/1)

Hotel Cambrils Playa

Child sharing main room

Durations	Up to 14/5 and 23/9 – 31/10	15/5 – 17/7 and 29/8 – 24/9	18/7 – 28/8
7 nights	£70	£90	£110
14 nights	£140	£180	£220

Hotel Cambrils Playa
Holiday Code   ANACG
Price base on   PB WC Balcony

Number of nights	7 Adult	14 Adult
01 May – 15 May	359	519
16 May – 04 Jun	389	559
05 Jun – 17 Jun	398	598
18 Jun – 01Jul	409	619
02 Jul – 11 Jul	419	639
12 Jul – 17 Jul	439	689
18 Jul – 05 Aug	519	759
06 Aug – 17 Aug	539	789
18 Aug – 27 Aug	539	789
28 Aug – 09 Sep	529	769
10 Sep – 23 Sep	459	719
24 Sep – 02 Oct	429	629
03 Oct – 31 Oct	379	549

Supplements
per person per night single room £9.00
Reductions
per night 3rd adult sharing £6.00
4th adult sharing £8.00

Caledonia Park

All inclusive
Prices are in £s per full fare paying passenger

Departures on or between	7 nts	10 nts	14 nts
1 May – 15 May	409	509	619
22 May – 4 June	429	529	669
5 June – 17 June	429	529	639
18 June – 1July	449	559	729
2 July – 11 July	479	599	749
12 July – 17 July	489	609	769
18 July – 5 August	519	629	789
6 August – 17 August	509	619	769
18 August – 27 August	499	609	749
28 August – 9 September	469	559	699
10 September – 23 September	449	549	669
24 September – 8 October	429	529	649
9 October – 31 October	459	559	669

Work out the cost of each of the following holidays.

❶ Two adults for 10 nights in Caledonia Park leaving on 18th June.

❷ Two adults for seven nights in Bali Rani resort leaving on 2 March and including the meal plan.

❸ Three adults for 14 nights at Cambrils Playa leaving on 23 June.

❹ Two adults and two children at Cambrils Playa leaving on 7 August for seven days?

❺ The Widget Plus Works rugby team and officials are planning a seven-day trip to Caledonia Park leaving on 25 September. The total number of people is 23 but the hotel has offered them four free places. What will be the total cost of the trip? The team are planning to share this cost equally. How much will each member pay?

9.5 Paying your way

In 1923 inflation was so bad in Germany that you would have needed a wheelbarrow to take home just one day's **wages**. Millions of marks were needed just for a loaf of bread! The photograph shows children playing with bundles of bank notes. These bundles were worth less than a set of toy building blocks!

- *Who do you think suffers most from inflation – the rich or the poor?*
- *What would you do if this sort of inflation happened in this country today?*

Pay rises

A **pay rise** is always welcome. Some people get a rise every year. Some people get a rise if they are promoted or complete a training course.

A worker is paid £200 a week for a 40-hour week. This is £5.00 an hour. Her union negotiates a pay rise with the employer of 4%. This means her wage rises by 4% of £200. What is her new wage?

4% means $\frac{4}{100}$ On a calculator you can write this as 0.04	
Multiply the starting wage by 4%:	£200 x 0.04 = £8
Add the answer to the original wage:	£200 + £8 = £208
The answer is:	£208.

How much will each of these weekly wages rise by?

① £200 with a 6% pay rise   ⑥ £190 with a 7% pay rise
② £300 with a 10% pay rise   ⑦ £100 with a 2% pay rise
③ £250 with a 2% pay rise   ⑧ £270 with a 5% pay rise
④ £200 with a 2% pay rise   ⑨ £180 with a 2% pay rise
⑤ £1000 with a 1% pay rise   ⑩ £750 with a 1% pay rise

What is the new weekly wage for each of these
people after their pay rise?

① £210 per week with a 5% increase   ⑥ £750 with a 3% increase
② £320.50 per week with a 20% increase   ⑦ £690 with a 7% increase
③ £125 per week with a 10% increase   ⑧ £1070 with a 6.5% increase
④ £350 per week with a 5% increase   ⑨ £209 with a 1.4% increase
⑤ £50 per week with a 25% increase   ⑩ £300 with a 6.7% increase

Bonus payments

Some people don't get a rise but they get a **bonus**. The bonus is
based on how well they have worked in the past year. A bonus is
often a percentage of the original salary.

A worker earns £35 000 in a year. His bonus is worth 45% of his final
salary. To find out his bonus multiply 35 000 by 45%. This gives a
figure of £15 750 which is paid at the end of the year.

45% means $\frac{45}{100}$. On a calculator you can write $\frac{45}{100}$ as 0.45.	
Multiply the starting wage by 45%:	35 000 x 0.45 = £15 750
The bonus is	£15 750
So, the total pay over the year is:	£35 000 + £15 750 = £50 750.

Copy out the table below and complete it. The first one has been done as
an example.

Annual pay	Bonus %	Bonus payment	Total pay and bonus
£10 000	5	£500	£10 500
① £26 000	3		
② £52 000	25		
③ £17 500	7		
④ £8 750	10		
⑤ £21 500	2		

43

Interesting

Payments on **loans** are linked to the size of the loan and the **interest** rate. Imagine you borrow £1000 for a year at an interest rate of 11% per year. How much will you have to pay back?

11% is 0.11 on a calculator.	
Multiply the £1000 loan by 11%:	£110.
Add the interest charged to the loan:	£1000 + £110 = £1110.
If you pay back a bit every month you divide the total by 12:	£1110 ÷ 12 = £92.50.
Monthly payments will be:	£92.50.

Calculate the monthly repayments for each of these loans. Each loan lasts for one year and has 12 equal payments.

❶ Borrowing £1200 at 19% per year
❷ Borrowing £6000 at 12% per year
❸ Borrowing £1800 at 15% per year
❹ Borrowing £2500 at 17% per year
❺ Borrowing £4000 at 14% per year
❻ Borrowing £9000 at 5% per year

A good deal?

Some companies offer special deals on loans. They say things like '£2000 to spend now for only £120 a month over two years'! Is this a good deal?

First you need to work out how much in total you will pay back. Multiply the payment value by the number of payments. 24 payments of £120 = £2880.
Then take the money you get away from the total: £2880 - £2000 = £880.
Total interest charged = £880 over two years. So, interest over one year is £880 - 2 = £440.
To work out the interest rate divide the amount of interest by the amount borrowed: £440 - 2000 = 0.22 = 22%. So, you pay 22% interest on your £2000 loan.

Work out the total paid back and the interest rate for each of these loans.

❶ £155 a month to borrow £1500 for one year.
❷ £200 a month to borrow £9000 for five years.
❸ £25 a month to borrow £250 for one year.
❹ £15 a week to borrow £624 for one year.
❺ £250 a month to borrow £10 000 for 10 years.

VAT at 17.5%

Value added tax or **VAT** is added to many of the things you buy. Usually shops add it in before they calculate the final price so you never see it. However, sometimes the prices are quoted excluding VAT.

How much VAT will you need to add to something which costs £1200? What will the new total price be?

Multiply the price by 17.5%:	£1200 x 0.175 = £210.
So, the VAT to be paid is	£210.
Add the VAT to the original price:	£1200 + £210 = £1410.

Printers	
Styleshot 2400	£99.99
Ink cartridge	£21.99
K-non Colour inkjet	£99.99
Epsan Colour inkjet	£109.99
Epsan ROM upgrade	£29.99
Epsan ink cartridges	£24.99

Calculate the total prices, including delivery and VAT for each of these orders.

1. Styleshot printer and one ink cartridge.
2. Epsan colour inkjet, the ROM upgrade and three extra ink cartridges.
3. EZO 17" monitor.
4. Iomo 100MB deluxe kit and seven extra cartridges.
5. A pack of 5 Iomo 100MB cartridges.

Monitors	
EZO 17"	£299
EZOi 17"	£349
Micro 15"	£179
Micro 17"	£329

Copy out the table below and complete it. The first one has been done as an example.

Item	Cost excluding VAT	VAT at 17.5%	Total cost
Washing machine	£400	£70	£470
1 Video recorder	£230		
2 Wet and dry cleaner	£70		
3 Electric sandwichmaker	£12		
4 Electric breadmaker	£60		
5 Garden chair	£26		

Removable storage	
Iomo 100MB kit	£120.99
Iomo 100MB deluxe kit	£179.99
100MB cartridges	£9.95 each
Pack of 5 cartridges	£42.99

All prices EXCLUDE VAT and delivery

Measuring, ordering and patterns

10.1 How long?

Cristo is an artist who wraps buildings in fabrics and calls it art. The photograph shows the Reichstag in Berlin wrapped in a type of silver foil! The whole thing is actually quite hard to do. Get the measurements wrong and you could end up with patches of bare building – or expensive fabrics left over!

- *Is this art or just messing about? Why?*
- *What is the strangest piece of art you've ever seen?*

What is the most sensible item to use to measure each of these lengths?

1. The width of a football pitch
2. The length of your exercise book
3. The length of a telephone box
4. The width of your bedroom
5. Your inside leg measurement
6. A piece of string

Measure the length of each of these lines accurately.

Find ten items that measure more than 30 cm but less than 1 m. Write down their names and then measure them accurately.

Measure each of these lengths accurately.
1. The width of your classroom
2. Your height
3. The height of the classroom door
4. The length of the blackboard
5. The width of a corridor
6. The width of a car parking space
7. The length of a car parking space
8. The height of a tennis net
9. The length of a basketball court
10. The height of the football goalposts

Sort these into ascending height order.
Explain how you made your decisions about the order.

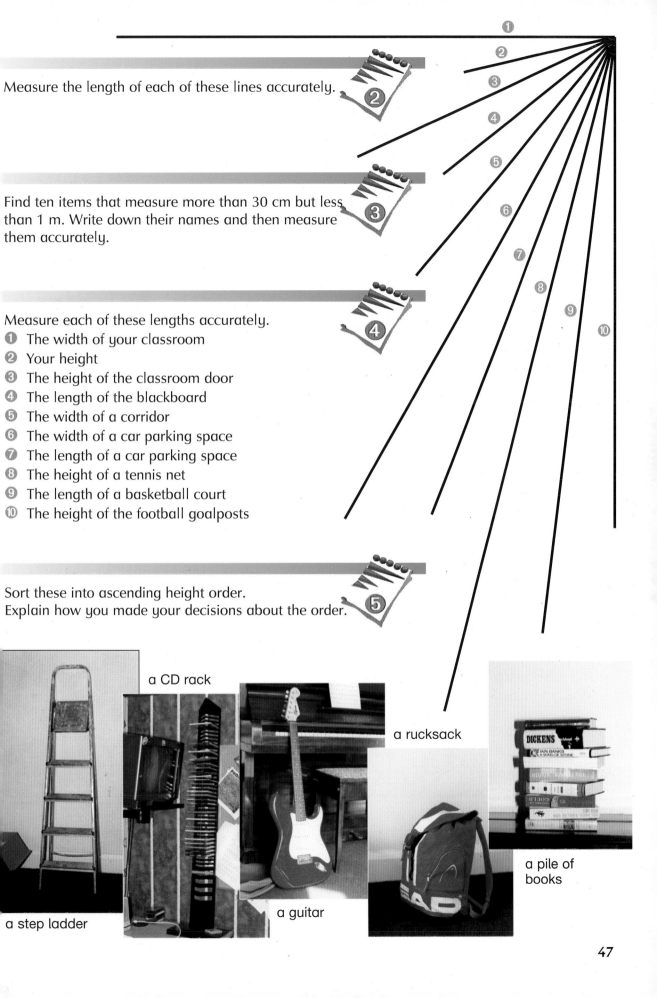

a CD rack

a rucksack

a pile of books

a guitar

a step ladder

10.2 Weight and capacity

Go-karting is serious racing. There are rules about the size of the engines to make sure that everyone has a fair chance in the race. Engine sizes are measured by volume – a typical go-kart would have a 0.3 litre engine. A small family car would be 1.4 litres.

- *Have you ever been go-karting? Would you like to?*
- *Go-karts are not allowed on the public road. Do you think this is fair? Why?*

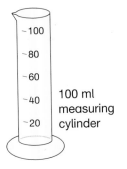

100 ml measuring cylinder

2 litre measuring jug

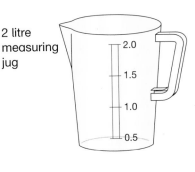

5 litre bucket

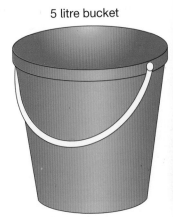

Choose the correct equipment to measure each of these amounts.

1. Water for a garden pond
2. 50 ml of milk for a recipe
3. 75 ml of water
4. A single dose of cough mixture
5. 350 ml of emulsion paint
6. 1 litre of engine oil

measuring spoons

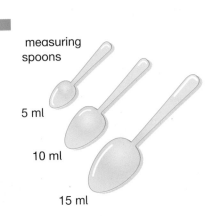

5 ml

10 ml

15 ml

Richard Branson is keen to be the first man to fly round the world in a balloon. His balloon Virgin Challenger is very carefully designed. The cabin where he lives with the pilot is strong and extremely lightweight. The lighter the cabin the better. Even the things that go into the cabin must be as light as possible.

Choose the correct equipment to measure each of these amounts.

1. The weight of an emergency radio
2. The weight of a small medical kit
3. The weight of a Sunday newspaper
4. The weight of an airmail letter
5. 15 tonnes of gravel
6. The weight of this book

0–100 g spring balance

0–3 kg kitchen scales

0–120 kg bathroom scales

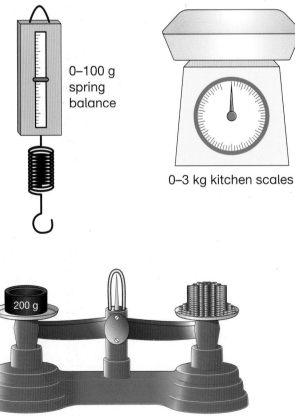

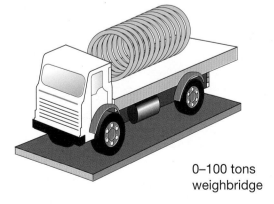

0–100 tons weighbridge

10.3 Estimating size

The pictures on this page give you a chance to check how good you are at estimating masses and capacities. All the answers are on page 2. How many can you get right?

5 good
6–8 very good
9–11 excellent
12 + did you cheat?

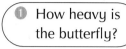
① How heavy is the butterfly?

② What is the capacity of the runner's lungs?

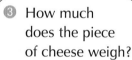
③ How much does the piece of cheese weigh?

④ What is the weight of these earrings?

⑤ How much does one hump weigh?

⑥ What is the capacity of the hump at the back?

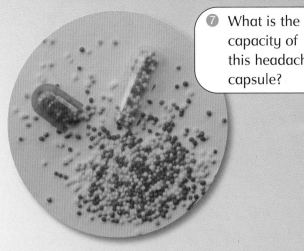

7 What is the capacity of this headache capsule?

8 What is the capacity of the brass watering can?

9 How heavy is this bird?

10 What is the capacity of one milk churn?

11 What is the capacity of the plastic compost barrel?

12 How much does it weigh when it is empty?

13 How much does a full milk churn weigh?

10.4 Number trails

Welcome, ladies and gentlemen, to *Figure it out!* This week we have six lovely contestants from across the country who will all get the chance to figure it out and win cash prizes. Two of them will go on to the grand final with the chance to win a fabulous, all-expenses-paid holiday! Let's meet our first contestants!

- *Which game show would you like to go on? Why?*
- *Have you ever won a prize in a competition? What was it?*

Contestants in *Figure it out* have to figure out what should go into the gaps in calculations.

Replace the * in the calculations below.
You can use +, –, x or ÷ to make the sum work.

1. 10 * 6 = 16
2. 20 * 7 = 13
3. 8 * 3 = 24
4. 27 * 9 = 3
5. 100 * 5 = 20
6. 90 * 27 = 63
7. 140 * 62 = 202
8. 47 * 21 = 68
9. 15 * 3 = 45
10. 56 * 7 = 8
11. 4 * 11 = 44
12. 18 * 3 = 54

In the grand final contestants are given a selection of numbers and a target number. They have to use the numbers and +, –, x or ÷ to reach the target. The person who gets there first is the winner. If no-one can solve the problem the person nearest the target when the time is up wins.

The numbers in red are the target numbers. How long does it take you to solve each problem?

1. 52   3   2   9   7
2. 27   4   2   7   3
3. 7   1   3   4   6
4. 26   9   2   3   5
5. 16   7   1   6   3

10.5 It all adds up!

Lucy the Hubcap Queen is only one of our crazy collectors!
People seem to be willing to collect anything and everything.
It all starts with one doll, or a pair of trainers or a hubcap...

- *Do you collect anything? What?*
- *Collecting is a hobby. What is your hobby?*

How many more hubcaps
will Lucy have in a year's time?
Look at the number pattern
to see if you can predict this.

3   6   9   12   15

$\searrow 3 \nearrow \searrow 3 \nearrow \searrow 3 \nearrow \searrow 3 \nearrow$

This tells you how quickly
Lucy's collection grows.

I get hubcaps from all over the
country. I usually get three every
week. It's amazing how kind local
scrap dealers are – they let me
salvage hubcaps and always give
me a good deal on the price.

Find the next number in each of these patterns. Explain how you
worked out your answers in each case.

①	5	10	15	20		⑥	2	5	8	11
②	6	12	18	24		⑦	5	7	9	11
③	10	20	30	40		⑧	12	16	20	24
④	25	50	75	100		⑨	6	10	14	18
⑤	30	60	90	120		⑩	4	7	10	13

Now work out the tenth term for each pattern.

Season tickets

I travel to work on the train most days. During the summer I ride a bicycle but I take the train if it's raining. Is it worth me getting a season ticket during the summer? A return train ticket costs £4 so if I go by train every day it soon starts to mount up: £4, £8, £12 and so on. The trouble is, a monthly travel pass costs £65.

❶ Write out the number pattern for the cost of John Jones' train journeys. When does it reach £65?

❷ How many journeys does he have to make each month to make buying a travel pass worthwhile?

❸ May was a very wet month in 1997. It rained so much that John Jones used the train 19 times during the month. How much did his journeys cost in total?

❹ How much would John Jones have saved if he had bought a monthly travel pass?

Find the next three numbers in each of these patterns. Show all your working.

❶	0	2	2	4	8	14	22
❷	0	7	21	42	70	105	147
❸	0	9	27	54	90	135	189
❹	0	11	33	66	110	165	231
❺	0	4	16	40	80	140	224

To work out number patterns start by looking at the differences between each number–- if you get a repeating pattern you can predict what number will come next. The simple pattern for Lucy's hubcaps works like this.

If the pattern is more complicated you may need to look at the differences between the differences. Think of it as working down a level. As soon as you find a pattern that you can predict you can build back up to the next number on the top row.

0   3   9   18   30   ?

0 ⟍3 ⟋⟍6 ⟋⟍9 ⟋⟍12 ⟋⟍15 ⟋

⟍3 ⟋⟍3 ⟋⟍3 ⟋⟍3 ⟋⟍3 ⟋

10.6 Getting less

This scene from the film *Alive* shows the survivors of an aircrash in the Andes mountains. The film is based on a true story. When their plane crashed they kept themselves alive over the winter by eating the passengers who had died. The only food in the airplane was packets of peanuts. The only drink was the free drinks from the aircraft bar. They were rescued the following spring after some of them set off down the mountain to look for help.

- *Where is the most dangerous place you have ever been?*
- *How did you keep safe?*

People need 1500 ml of water every day. If a person is stranded somewhere with 7000 ml of water how much will he or she have left after one day?
7000 - 1500 = 5500.

And after two days:
5500 - 1500 = 4000.

And after three days:
4000 - 1500 = 2500.

The sequence for the changes in water supply is:

7000   5500   4000   2500   (?)
　↘1500 ↗↘ 1500 ↗↘ 1500 ↗↘1500 ↗

Find the next number in each of these patterns. Explain how you worked out your answers in each case.

❶	1000	900	800	❻	45	41	37
❷	80	75	70	❼	26	24	22
❸	92	90	88	❽	39	36	33
❹	65	63	61	❾	150	135	120
❺	100	93	86	❿	100	89	78

Now work out the tenth term for each pattern.

10.7 Doubling and halving

Bacteria multiply by splitting into two. If conditions are right, each bacterium splits about every 30 minutes. So, if you start with one, you will have two after 30 minutes – and four after 60 minutes. Bacteria divide fastest when it is warm and damp. The bacteria in our bodies help to make them decay after we die.

The preserved body here has survived because ice in the mountains where he lived prevented bacteria from growing. The boy was an Inca sacrifice from 500 years ago.

- *How can you tell if food has 'gone off'?*
- *Why does food keep fresh longer in a refrigerator?*

Amounts change very quickly by doubling. Imagine a set of one centimetre squares. Put one down and then put two underneath it. Now add a line of four underneath them. Now add a line of eight under the four and so on. By the time you have seven lines your bottom line will be over a metre long. By the time you have 17 lines the bottom line will be over a kilometre long. By 20 lines it will be over 10 km and by 30 lines it will be over 10 000 km!

Find the next number in each of these patterns. Explain how you worked out your answers in each case.

❶	3	6	12	24		❼	9	18	36	72
❷	5	10	20	40		❽	50	100	200	400
❸	2	4	8	16		❾	200	400	800	1600
❹	10	20	40	80		❿	13	26	52	104
❺	8	16	32	64		⓫	11	22	44	88
❻	7	14	28	56		⓬	19	38	76	152

Now work out the tenth term for each pattern.

Radioactive waste

Nuclear power stations produce waste which is radioactive. This waste causes cancer and other illnesses in living things. All we can do is store it until it is not dangerous any more. A pile of radioactive waste decays naturally to safer substances.

A 200 g lump of uranium will change into 100 g of uranium and 100 g of lead in 4500 million years. The 100 g of uranium changes to 50 g of uranium and 50 g of lead in another 4500 million years. 4500 million years is called the 'half life'.
Different sorts of waste have different half lives. Scientists can use this pattern to predict when a pile of radioactive waste will become safe.

At the moment we have thousands of tonnes of radioactive waste which will become safe in millions of years. Until then we have to store it safely away from people and other living things.

Find the next number in each of these patterns.
Explain how you worked out your answers in each case.

❶	1600	800	400
❷	64	32	16
❸	320	160	80
❹	384	192	96
❺	480	240	120
❻	1664	832	416
❼	1088	544	272
❽	352	176	88
❾	6144	3072	1536
❿	1344	672	336
⓫	608	304	152
⓬	30720	15360	7680

Now work out the sixth value for each pattern.

11 Quantities

11.1 Jungle assignment

It is possible to go on holiday in the rainforest now. The jungles are still beautiful and unspoilt. However, if we disturb the area too much that beauty will be lost. You have to walk through the jungle carrying your supplies with you – even your camera equipment. If you are only allowed 1500 g what will you take?

- *Would you like to visit a rainforest? Why?*
- *At what other times would you need to make decisions about weights for carrying?*

You need to take at least three different lenses. Which lenses would you choose for each of the weight limits below? The camera body weighs 1250 g and does not count towards these weights.

❶ 1000 g   ❹ 1200 g
❷ 2000 g   ❺ 2200 g
❸ 2500 g   ❻ 3000 g

Lenses	Weight / g
Wide angle	470
Super wide angle	225
Standard	240
Telephoto	570
Super telephoto	785
Zoom	1010
Power zoom	800
Close-up	695
Soft focus	190

Find the total of the following weights.

❶ 64 g	17 g	180 g	95 g	210 g
❷ 124 g	96 g	83 g	324 g	75 g
❸ 480 g	310 g	6 g	19 g	49 g
❹ 68 g	710 g	17 g	51 g	8 g
❺ 125 g	75 g	325 g	61 g	32 g

List at least five ways to make a total weight of 1 kg.
You can use the weights shown in the diagram below.

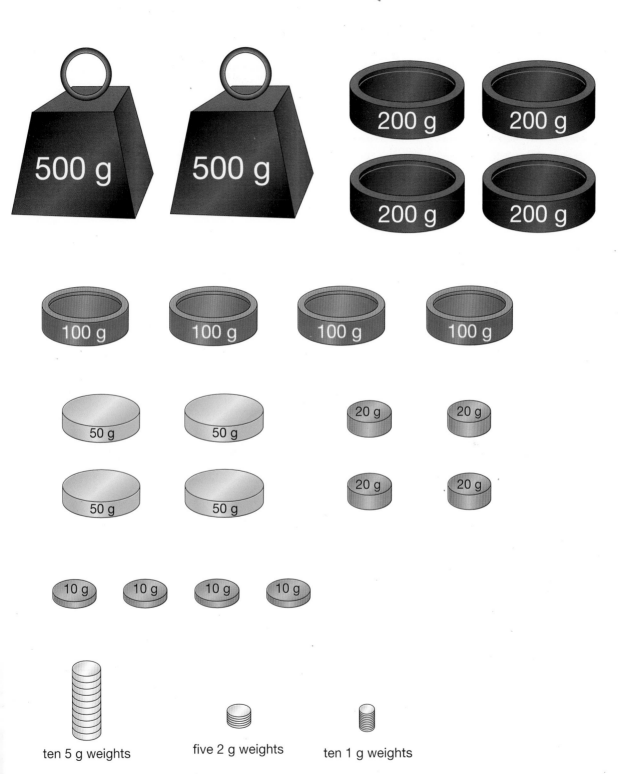

ten 5 g weights

five 2 g weights

ten 1 g weights

5250 g Start with the weight in grams.

5250 g = 5000 g + 250g

5000 g = 5 kg

5250 = 5 kg 250 g

Convert each of these weights into kg and g.

❶ 5490 g   ❺ 5500 g   ❾ 1010 g

❷ 4390 g   ❻ 6200 g   ❿ 2025 g

❸ 6721 g   ❼ 7250 g   ⓫ 3005 g

❹ 3000 g   ❽ 8100 g   ⓬

3 kg 200 g Start with the weight in kilograms and grams.

3 kg = 3000 g

3000 g + 200 g = 3200 g

Convert each of these weights from kg and g into g.

❶ 4 kg 120 g   ❺ 8 kg 150 g   ❾ 9 kg 86 g

❷ 4 kg 500 g   ❻ 2 kg 310 g   ❿ 2 kg 11 g

❸ 2 kg 150 g   ❼ 8 kg 115 g   ⓫ 5 kg 5 g

❹ 1 kg 710 g   ❽ 3 kg 60 g   ⓬

Find the sum of these weights.

1. 65 g   1 kg 200 g   850 g   17 g
2. 3 kg 500 g   1 kg 60 g   710 g   86 g
3. 2 kg 55 g   3 kg 200 g   650 g   78 g
4. 5 kg   2 kg 75 g   320 g   1 kg 165 g
5. 965 g   1 kg 20 g   44 g   3 kg 289 g

Small babies do not always mean small adults. How many times bigger are these adults compared with their babies? You will need to convert both measurements to the same units and then divide the adult weight by the bay weight.

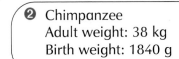

2. Chimpanzee
   Adult weight: 38 kg
   Birth weight: 1840 g

1. Frankenstein's monster
   Adult weight: 198 kg
   Birth weight: 198 kg

3. Black bear
   Adult weight: 115 000 g
   Birth weight: 0.4 kg

4. Giraffe
   Adult weight: 1400 kg
   Birth weight: 350 000 g

5. Human being
   Adult weight: 79 kg
   Birth weight: 3200 g

11.2 Weightlifter

Are weightlifters the ugliest athletes? This one is lifting weights that weigh more than he does! He has trained for years for a lift which could last less than five seconds. The total weight on the bar is found by adding the values of all the separate weights.

- *What is the heaviest thing you have ever lifted?*
- *Would you like to look like this weightlifter? Why?*

How much is the weightlifter lifting in each of these? Remember you can only see one half of the total weight.

❶

❹

❷

❺

❸

❻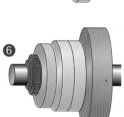

1.25
2.5
5.0
7.5
10
15
20
25

11.3 Animal farm

This Highland cow looks cute – but smells as bad as any other cow!
This may be due to the tonnes of grass it eats during its lifetime!
Mind you, farmers like animals that eat well and grow quickly.

- *Why do you think farmers prefer cows that grow quickly?*
- *Can you think of an advantage for a slow-growing animal?*

Arrange these animal weights into ascending order.

❶	500 g	650 g	2 kg	425 g
❷	1 kg	850 g	2500 g	900 g
❸	4 kg	420 g	4200 g	5 kg
❹	150 g	75 g	7 kg	500 g
❺	3 kg	4000 g	350 g	300 g

Arrange these animal weights into descending order.

❶	300 g	750 g	2 kg	425 g
❷	60 g	6 kg	650 g	6200 g
❸	470 g	4 kg	4700 g	400 g
❹	80 g	850 g	8 kg	8500 g
❺	35 g	3 g	3000 g	2 kg

11.4 Capacities

The bee hummingbird is the smallest in the world. It weighs only a few grammes and lays an egg that contains less than 1 ml of yolk. The ostrich is one of the biggest birds in the world and lays eggs that can be a hundred times heavier than an adult hummingbird! A typical ostrich egg contains over 1000 ml of yolk.

- *What is the biggest egg you have ever seen?*
- *Would you eat an omelette made from an ostrich egg?*

Convert these capacities from cl to litres.

❶ 350 cl	❺ 240 cl	❾ 495 cl
❷ 600 cl	❻ 770 cl	❿ 627 cl
❸ 800 cl	❼ 824 cl	⓫ 882 cl
❹ 450 cl	❽ 632 cl	⓬ 999 cl

Convert these capacities from litres to cl.

❶ 5 l	❺ 9.5 l	❾ 3.05 l
❷ 3 l	❻ 10.25 l	❿ 12.07 l
❸ 6.8 l	❼ 18.82 l	⓫ 107.09 l
❹ 7.2 l	❽ 5.48 l	⓬ 11.14 l

Find the total of these capacities.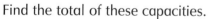

❶ 3 l	650 cl	2.5 l	55 cl
❷ 2 l	305 cl	850 cl	2.9 l
❸ 165 cl	527 cl	7 l	6 l
❹ 99 cl	1.5 l	100 cl	250 cl
❺ 40 cl	5 l	4.2 l	610 cl

11.5 Sensible units

All of the measurements on this page are correct – but some of the units are rather strange. Re-write the caption for each picture with more sensible units.

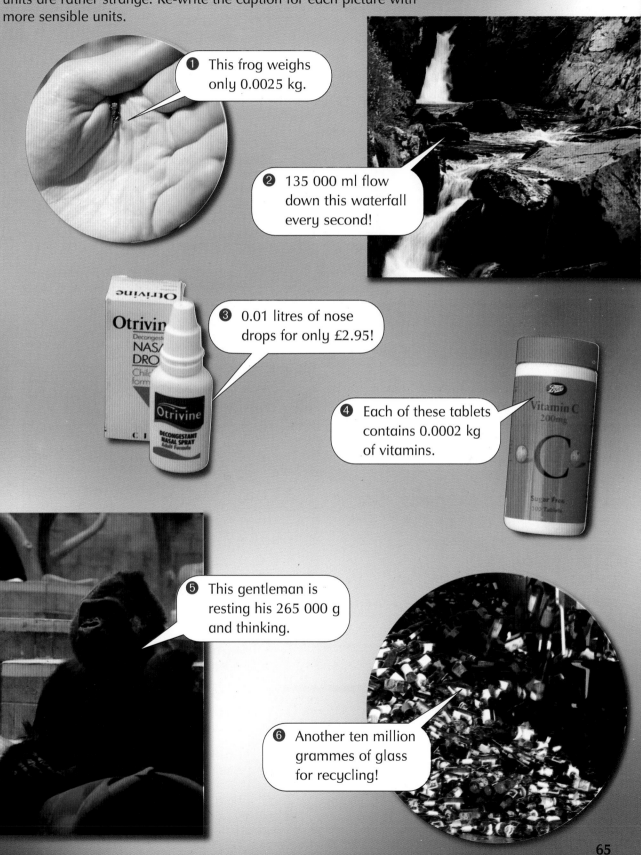

❶ This frog weighs only 0.0025 kg.

❷ 135 000 ml flow down this waterfall every second!

❸ 0.01 litres of nose drops for only £2.95!

❹ Each of these tablets contains 0.0002 kg of vitamins.

❺ This gentleman is resting his 265 000 g and thinking.

❻ Another ten million grammes of glass for recycling!

11.6 Cooking times

When you cook meat you have to be sure that it gets cooked all the way through. Otherwise it may not be safe to eat. It doesn't take long to cook a burger, but how long is long enough?

- *Do you eat meat? Why?*
- *Have you ever eaten meat at a barbecue?*

Start with the weight in kg: 1 kg

Multiply the weight by the times per kg: 5 x 40 = 200 min

Now add any extra time: 200 + 20 = 220 min

The table shows guide times for cooking various joints of meat.

Meat	Cooking time in minutes
Chicken	40 / kg + 20
Beef	50 / kg + 10
Lamb	45 / kg + 15
Pork	50 / kg + 15

Calculate the length of time needed to cook the following joints of meat.

❶ Chicken 2 kg ❺ Beef 2.5 kg ❾ Beef 3.5 kg
❷ Lamb 2 kg ❻ Pork 2.5 kg ❿ Chicken 2.5 kg
❸ Beef 3 kg ❼ Chicken 3 kg ⓫ Chicken 1.5 kg
❹ Pork 3 kg ❽ Lamb 3.5 kg ⓬ Beef 4 kg

The table shows guide times for cooking various joints of meat.

Meat	Cooking time in minutes
Chicken Beef Lamb Pork	20 / lb + 20 25 / lb + 15 20 / lb + 25 25 / lb + 10

Calculate the length of time needed to cook the following joints of meat.

❶ Beef 3 lb ❺ Beef 4 lb ❾ Chicken 4.5 lb
❷ Pork 3 lb ❻ Pork 4 lb ❿ Lamb 2.5 lb
❸ Lamb 4 lb ❼ Lamb 3.5 lb ⓫ Lamb 3 lb
❹ Chicken 5 lb ❽ Beef 2 lb ⓬ Pork 5 lb

Using the cooking times given in the previous two exercises, calculate the time that you would need to start cooking each of these joints for them to be ready by the time given.

Meat	Weight	Finishing time
❶ Chicken	3 lb	5.20 pm
❷ Beef	2 kg	5.40 pm
❸ Lamb	2 kg	6.00 pm
❹ Pork	4 lb	7.00 pm
❺ Beef	3 lb	5.30 pm

11.7 Cooking for a crowd

Cooking for the crowd at this outdoor wedding isn't easy. The kitchen is just a large tent and all your recipes have to be scaled up to cope with all the people.

- *What is the largest number you have ever cooked for?*
- *What problems did that number of people cause you?*

Recipes

Sweet and sour pork (serves 4)
- 2 tablespoons soya sauce
- 2 tablespoons rice wine
- 2 cloves garlic
- 1 teaspoon crushed ginger
- 450 g pork fillet
- 2 tablespoons vinegar
- 1 tablespoon cornflour
- 2 tablespoons tomato sauce
- 3 tablespoons clear honey
- 2 tablespoons vegetable oil
- 2 peppers

Taramasalata (serves 8)
- 225 g smoked cod's roe
- 12 tablespoons olive oil
- juice of 1 lemon
- 1 teaspoon grated onion
- 1 teaspoon chopped parsley

Boeuf en croute (serves 6)
- 900 g fillet of beef
- 2 rashers bacon
- 225 g mushrooms
- 50 g butter
- 325 g puff pastry

Chicken casserole (serves 6)
- 2 tablespoons oil
- 600 g chicken pieces
- 4 potatoes
- 180 ml chicken stock
- 2 rashers bacon
- 2 cloves garlic
- 60 ml white wine

Blackcurrant sorbet (serves 4)
- 300 ml water
- 100 g sugar
- 225 g blackcurrants
- 1 teaspoon lemon juice
- 2 egg whites

Chilli beef (serves 4)
- 450 g minced beef
- 1 level teaspoon chilli powder
- 1 onion (small)
- 350 g kidney beans
- 250 g tinned tomatoes
- 1 tablespoon Worcestershire sauce

Rewrite each of these recipes to serve double the amount given in the recipe.

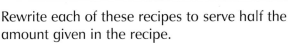

❶ Beef en croute
❷ Sweet and sour pork
❸ Chicken casserole
❹ Blackcurrant sorbet
❺ Shiro wot
❻ Zom
❼ Chilli beef
❽ Sweet potato rice

Rewrite each of these recipes to serve half the amount given in the recipe.

❶ Taramasalata
❷ Chilli beef
❸ Chicken casserole
❹ Beef en croute
❺ Paw-paw and mango fool
❻ Shiro wot
❼ Zom
❽ Hummus

Rewrite each of these recipes to serve 12 people.

❶ Chilli beef
❷ Blackcurrant sorbet
❸ Zom
❹ Taramasalata
❺ Shiro wot
❻ Sweet and sour pork
❼ Paw-paw and mango fool
❽ Chicken casserole

Shiro wot (serves 2)
    250 g peanuts
    50 g margarine
    1 small onion
    1 tablespoon tomato paste
    1/2 teaspoon dried thyme
    1/2 teaspoon ground mixed spice
    1 teaspoon paprika
    300 ml water

Zom (serves 8)
    900 g stewing beef
    4 tablespoons oil
    1 large onion
    900 g fresh spinach
    2 tomatoes
    1 tablespoon tomato paste
    2 tablespoons peanut butter

Paw-paw and mango fool (serves 4)
    200 g paw-paw
    200 g mango
    2 tablespoons lemon juice
    120 ml double cream
    50 g sugar

Sweet potato pie (serves 4)
    450 g sweet potatoes
    1 medium can pineapple chunks
    2 tablespoons melted margarine
    1/2 teaspoon ground cloves
    1/2 tablespoon lemon juice
    50 g breadcrumbs or toasted oats

Hummus (serves 4)
    250 g chickpeas, soaked and cooked
    2 cloves garlic, crushed
    1 tablespoon tahini
    juice of 2 lemons
    25 ml olive oil

12 Practical tasks

12.1 How to do an investigation

You will use mathematics to solve many everyday problems. It is a good idea to have a system to help you tackle these problems. The traffic light sign will help you to remember to do everything you need – and get it all in the correct order.

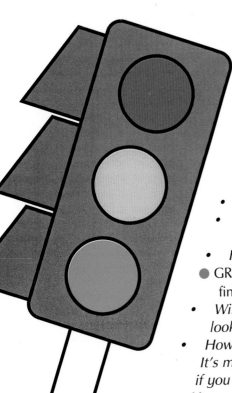

● RED: Stop! Think before you start.
- *What is your task called? Give it a title that tells you something about what you are investigating.*
- *What exactly do you want to find out? Write down any ideas you have about what might happen.*

● ORANGE: Get ready!
- *What equipment will you need? Think about measuring equipment, graph or squared paper, maybe a computer or calculator?*
- *Make a plan to guide your work.*
- *How will you collect your data? A table for results is very useful – make one before you start.*
- *Has your teacher checked your plan?*

● GREEN: Go! But be careful. Don't rush and make sure you finish everything properly.
- *Will you need to change your plan? Keep thinking and look out for surprises.*
- *How much data will you need to answer your question? It's much more difficut to come back and do the work again if you don't gather enough data the first time round.*
- *How will you tell people about your results? A clear write-up must include all your data and an explanation of what it means. Often a diagram or a chart will help.*

Use the traffic light idea to check this task.

Ben and Chris play a game with one dice. The rules are simple. Ben rolls the dice and if the number is less than four he scores a point. If the number is an even number then Chris scores a point. For some results they could both score. Next time, Chris rolls the dice and the same rules apply. The first person to get five points is the winner.

The question they need to answer is 'Does the person who rolls first have an advantage?' At the moment they think it doesn't matter.

These questions help you to see if Chris and Ben know what they were going to do.

❶ What were Chris and Ben trying to find out?
❷ Did they have an idea about what would happen? What was it?

They decided to play the game to see who won. Sometimes they tried it with Ben starting. Then they tried it with Chris starting. After ten games they got these results.

Game	Who started?	Who won?
1	Ben	Ben
2	Chris	Ben
3	Ben	Chris
4	Chris	Chris
5	Ben	Chris
6	Chris	Ben
7	Ben	Chris
8	Chris	Ben
9	Ben	Ben
10	Chris	Chris

They decided that it looked as though they were right. Whoever started made no difference. They looked to see if they could work out why.

These questions help you to see if Chris and Ben planned their task carefully enough.

❶ What did Ben and Chris plan to do?
❷ List the equipment they would need to carry out their plan.
❸ How did their plan change during the task?
❹ How many times did they play the game? Do you think this is enough? Why?
❺ They decided to draw a chart to show how many games they each won. Which sort of chart would be best? Why?

Ben said that whoever rolled the dice the chance of getting any particular number was always the same. The chance of getting a '1' was ⅙ every time. Since the person who rolled the dice did not matter the only question left was whether the scoring was fair.

Ben would score if the dice turned up a 1, 2 or 3. So, the chance that Ben would score was: ⅙ + ⅙ + ⅙ = ½.

Chris would score if the dice turned up a 2, 4 or 6. So, the chance that Chris would score a point was: ⅙ + ⅙ + ⅙ = ½.

So, the chance of either player scoring was always ½ or 50%. This meant the game had to be fair – if the dice was fair.

These questions help you to see if Chris and Ben completed their task properly.

❶ Write down how Ben and Chris worked out that their game had to be fair.
❷ Look at the results they collected. Do they agree with their idea?
❸ Do you agree with their idea? Explain why.
❹ Do you think they did their task well? Could you have done it better? How?

All investigations in this unit have a traffic light symbol. Most of the exercises in *Maths Plus* can be done in a short time on one sheet of paper. Investigations usually take much longer - perhaps a week or two. You will probably use more than one sheet of paper and may have to do work outside the classroom. The investigation symbol should remind you to do enough work to get good marks.

- ● RED: Stop! Think before you start.
- ● ORANGE: Get ready!
- ● GREEN: Go! But be careful.
               Don't rush and make sure you finish.

Ben and Chris believe the dice they used was fair. Plan and carry out an investigation to see if they were right. Make sure you follow the traffic light rule!

12.2 Planning a party

People make a fortune just putting on parties. The tickets to this party in Ibiza could cost over £10 each. The organisers have to pay for entertainment, the rent for the venue and any food and drink supplied. How many tickets do you need to sell to make a profit?

- *Have you ever been to a ticket-only party? How much did it cost to get in?*
- *Was it worth the ticket price? Why?*

You are in charge of planning an end-of-year party for 100 people. You will need to decide on all the details. Music, food, venue, tickets, etc. are all your job!

How much will you have to charge for a ticket? Work out how much the whole event will cost. Then work out how much the tickets must be to cover your costs. Plan carefully – you will have lots of data to handle and mistakes could be expensive!

12.3 Student digs

This house is going to be converted into student rooms. The rooms will be homes for students while they do their college courses. Many people leave home now to go on courses or training schemes.

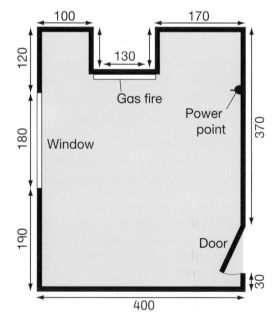

- *Do you expect to go somewhere to study or train?*
- *What sorts of things would you want in your student room?*

You have to design a suitable room for a student. Use scale diagrams and drawings to show how it will look when you have finished. Remember that students will need room to study and somewhere to keep clothes and valuables.

You will need to produce a list of all the items you want to buy with their costs. A spreadsheet may be useful to keep track of the totals.

Produce a fully-costed plan to convert the student room on this page. The budget is £200 to redecorate the room and another £500 for furniture.

12.4 Shopping survey

Shopping malls get bigger and more complicated every year! Some have complete funfairs inside them. Soon, you won't need to leave the shopping centre for anything!

- *Where does your family do most of its shopping?*
- *Do you think this a sensible choice? Why?*

Find out which shops give the best value for your weekly shop. You will need to produce a list of your normal groceries and price them up in different shops. A spreadsheet may help to total up of prices. When you are ready you will have to produce a recommendation of which shop gives you the best value.

You may find some things are cheaper in some shops so you ought to go to a range of shops to get the cheapest possible groceries. What is the lowest possible price for your complete list – if you choose items from a range of shops? Is cost the only thing that is important to you?

Produce a total cost for your weekly shop and show where you would buy each item. Show how to cut the cost even further – if you can!

12.5 Traffic survey

Every year millions of vehicles drive through our towns and cities. The area covered by roads, car parks and garages goes up all the time. The car is taking over the places where we live. Is this a good thing?

- *What are the advantages of owning a car?*
- *What are the disadvantages?*

How much traffic is there outside your home or school? Is this too busy? Which places have the greatest traffic flow? How busy are these areas compared with quieter streets? Twice as busy? Or four times? Or ten times?

Pedestrian precincts are now common in towns. What would happen to the traffic in your area if cars were banned from one street? Which street would you choose – and why? You will need to use data to support your ideas.

Carry out a survey of traffic flow in your area. Suggest one way to change the traffic flow. Explain how this will affect the number of cars in your street.

12.6 Uniform

Police officers wear uniforms so that we can recognise them in a crowd. This gives us confidence. We know who to turn to in a crisis!

- *Who else wears a uniform to make them instantly recognisable?*
- *Many schools still have uniforms. Do you think this is a good idea? Why?*

Uniforms are useful – but expensive. Choose a shop and design a suitable uniform. Remember that you need to provide two outfits for everyone in the shop – one to wear while the other is being washed. There may be different uniforms for male and female shop assistants. You may need extra uniforms for people who do casual work in the summer.

When you have decided on the best uniform you will need to work out how much it would cost per assistant. Then you can give the shop manager a complete cost to put everyone in uniform.

Work out how much it would cost to provide a uniform for everyone at a shop in your area. Show how you worked out this cost.

12.7 Take-away cartons

Chips may taste better from newspaper but it's getting more and more difficult for chip shops to collect paper. More and more people recycle their old newspapers now.

- *Chip shop chips do taste best. Do you agree?*
- *Newspaper wrapping is a bad idea. It is messy and covers your fingers with ink. What do you think?*

Find out how different take-away food shops wrap up their food. Which ones have the best solution to the problem of keeping the foods hot at the lowest possible packaging price?

Design a new carton for a take-away food shop. The carton must be:
- made from a single sheet of card or paper
- easy to assemble in a hurry
- hold the food in without spilling
- cheap to make with no wasted paper or card
- easy to fold flat to throw away.

Test a few different designs and choose the best. Draw a net of your final design so that the manufacturer can design a machine to cut the card or paper to shape.

12.8 Carpet heaven?

New homes often come with carpets. This means people don't have another big bill as soon as they move in. But what happens if you don't like the carpets the builder supplies?

- *Would you prefer a home with carpets included in the price or not? Why?*
- *What are the disadvantages of taking fitted carpets away with you when you move home?*

Carpet Heaven Ltd has hundreds of carpets at lots of different prices. The sales representatives there say that they can sell you the carpets for your new home more cheaply than the builder. The builder pays £2000 for all the carpets in a house. Can you get the carpets you need for less than this price?

Use the plans of your new home to work out how much carpet you will need. Try some of your local carpet stores to see if you can carpet it for less than £2000.

When you have finished your task you should have a detailed quote showing how much carpet, and underlay, you need and how much it will all cost.

Glossary

acute angle	smaller than 90°
bonus	a sum added once to the weekly or monthly wage
co-ordinates	numbers which describe the place a point occupies in a grid
command	instruction
corner	where two lines or sides meet
edge	border
equilateral triangle	triangle with all sides of the same length
estimate	the same as approximate
face	surface
interest	a percentage of the loan paid as the fee for borrowing
isosceles triangle	triangle with two sides of the same length
kite	four-sided shape with no parallel sides but two pairs of sides of the same length
leap year	every fourth year when February has 29 days
line of symmetry	the mirror line on a shape
loan	borrowed money
net	flat pattern for a three-dimensional shape
obtuse angle	between 90° and 180°
parallelogram	shape with four sides, with opposite sides parallel and equal in length
pay rise	an increase to a regular wage
program	a collection of commands
quadrilateral	shape with four sides
rectangle	four-sided shape with opposite sides parallel and of the same length and all angle 90°
reflex angle	between 180° and 360°
rhombus	four-sided shape with all sides of the same length with opposite sides parallel and opposite angle equal
right angle	a 90° angle
rotate	to turn with a circular movement
scale model	a proportionally smaller version
scalene triangle	triangle with sides of three different lengths
square	shape with sides of the same length and equal angles
symmetry	when two halves on either side of a line are the same but mirror images of each other
tessellation	to fit together without any gaps
three-dimensional	with faces in three different directions
trapezium	a four-sided shape with only one pair of parallel sides
triangle	shape with three straight sides
VAT	tax of 17.5% added to some prices
wage	regular weekly payment for a job